CONTENTS

Home Office/Scottish Office

GUIDE TO SAFETY AT SPORTS GROUNDS

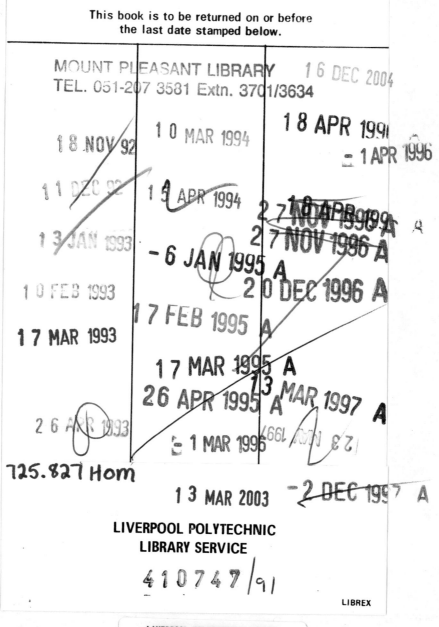
London: HMSO

ISBN 0 11 341001 8

ANNEXES

1. INTRODUCTION

Scope and Status of the Guide

1.   The object of this document is to give guidance to ground management, local authorities and technical specialists such as engineers in order to assist them to assess how many spectators can be safely accommodated within a sports ground used for a sporting event. The document also outlines measures for improving safety at existing grounds. The Guide has no statutory force but many of its recommendations will be made statutory at individual grounds by their inclusion in safety certificates issued under the Safety of Sports Grounds Act 1975 or the Fire Safety and Safety of Places of Sport Act 1987.

2.   Whether or not a ground is the subject of a safety certificate, ground operators, who have primary responsibility for the safety of their spectators, should apply the criteria, enlisting professional expertise, where necessary, in order to help ensure safe conditions at their ground.

Background to the Guide

3.   Guidelines on measures for improving the safety of spectators at sports grounds first became available when the Wheatley Report on Crowd Safety at Sports Grounds was published in 1972. The recommendations in the Appendix to that Report were extended to include fire precautions and means of escape from an emergency situation. They formed the basis of the first Guide to Safety at Sports Grounds and continue to do so.

4.   The application of the original guidelines to football grounds revealed a need for advice to be amended in certain respects. Furthermore, since the safety of spectators can be affected when crowds are disturbed by hooligan elements, the recommendations of the Working Party on Crowd Behaviour were incorporated in a new version, published in 1976, which was aimed specifically at football grounds.

5.   Following the fire at Bradford City FC ground in 1985, a working party, established under the aegis of Mr Justice Popplewell's Inquiry into Crowd Safety and Control at Sports Grounds, reviewed the Guide and produced a series of recommendations which were taken into account in consultation with others to produce a revised and expanded second edition in 1986.

6.   This third edition incorporates further changes made following re-examination of the guidelines in the light of recommendations by the Inquiry by Lord Justice Taylor who reviewed the guide with technical assistance in the course of his inquiry into the tragedy at Hillsborough in 1989.

Historical context

7.   Serious accidents at sports grounds involving injuries on a large scale are fortunately few. But as demonstrated by those at Burnden Park in 1946, Ibrox Stadium in 1971, Valley Parade in 1985 and Hillsborough in 1989, the potential for disaster at a crowded sporting event is such that it is essential for ground management to ensure reasonable safety at their grounds. This applies to all grounds irrespective of the sport being played and whether or not they are the subject of a safety certificate.

General principles of the Guide

8.   The problem of crowd safety at sports grounds is complex and cannot be solved simply by ensuring that individual components of a ground, such as stairways, passages or sections of terracing, are satisfactory in themselves. The inter-relation of these and other components is critical: none of them can be considered in isolation without consideration of its effect on the others. They should all be compatible and combine to form a balanced unit.

9.   The guide is intended to cover grounds where sporting events of all kinds are held and where the gathering of large crowds is likely to present a safety problem. Football has had particular problems which are not normally experienced to the same extent elsewhere. Accordingly, much of the guidance has particular application to football grounds. But whatever the sport it should be recognised that crowd problems are often directly related to the nature of the event and the numbers attending it.

10. The variety of type, function and layout of sports grounds and the inter-relationship of the different components means that a flexible approach should be maintained to take account of the individual nature of grounds. The Guide does not attempt to provide a universal minimum standard but sets achievable standards. It may therefore be possible to deviate from individual guidelines without detracting from the overall safety of the ground. Any decision to do so should be properly recorded with supporting documentation and adhered to. But unless other measures, which can be demonstrated to achieve an equal or greater degree of safety are taken, a reduction of the numbers of spectators, compared to the number who would otherwise be accommodated, will be required. That reduction may be severe.

11. The Guide is aimed primarily at safety in existing sports grounds and therefore attempts to take account of the constraints and difficulties which are present in these grounds. It is not a design brief for new construction work or reconstruction work at sports grounds, but the standards of such work should not be lower than those set out in the Guide. New work should conform to the appropriate Building Regulations. The scope of new design work should lead to higher standards of safety and amenity than those that can be achieved at grounds already built.

12. When using the Guide to assess whether existing circumstances provide adequately for the safety of spectators, the criterion to be aimed for is that of a reasonable degree of safety. It would be unreasonable, if not impractical, to seek standards for absolute safety of everyone attending a ground.

13. The Guide is not specifically aimed at risks to spectators from the sport itself, but managements have a duty to take all necessary precautions to safeguard spectators against the effects of accidents in, or originating from, the activity on the track or the playing area. Particular care is needed when the sport entails the use and storage of flammable fuels.

14. The advice given in this Guide is without prejudice to the operation of the Building Act, Building Regulations, the Health and Safety at Work etc Act 1974 and any other relevant legislation.

Using the Guide
15. *The Guide is an aid to professional judgement and common sense,* not a substitute. The principles referred to in paragraphs 8-14 above should be kept in mind by both ground management and, where applicable, by the local authority when applying the Guide to an individual ground.

16. Although some of the safety standards are likely to apply to all sports grounds however many spectators are present, it is nevertheless important to relate the Guide to the needs of each individual ground. The required safety standard to be attained should relate to the maximum number of spectators who are to be admitted to the ground or parts of it. For example, a football ground with a maximum spectator capacity of tens of thousands is likely to pose significant crowd pressure risks particularly if it is full or nearly full. To accommodate such a crowd safely may necessitate substantial remedial work. Alternatively, consideration might be given to accepting a much smaller number of spectators who, properly dispersed, could be accommodated safely without having to incur costly repairs, improvements or alterations. Therefore, the first step, using the Guide's criteria, is to assess how many spectators can be accommodated safely given the existing condition of the ground. In other words, determine a safe ground capacity based on each section of viewing accommodation, entry and exit route. This requires properly detailed plans drawn to scale (1:200) of the ground.

The problems
17. There are essentially four types of safety problem to be considered within a ground and its immediate surroundings, all of which are inter-related.

18. *Underfoot conditions:* The first hazard is tripping or falling which may have serious consequences for the individual concerned, but can also lead to a serious incident involving others. This type of problem can be remedied by proper care maintenance; and attention to good building practice.

19. *Crowd pressures:* The second type involves crowd pressures and is potentially the more serious. Careful attention must be paid to avoid overcrowding, to restrain surges and similar pressures on the terraces, and to ensure free movement throughout the entry/exit systems. When large crowds are present and densities are high, pressures build up within the crowd either through motion or swaying which make it difficult, or even impossible, for individuals to control their own movements. Under these conditions crowd pressures can escalate to a dangerous level and if a person stumbles or falls the crowd cannot adapt to avoid them or to stop to help. Since this type of danger arises from crowd pressures its remedy lies in their removal or restraint within safe limits. These dangers arise particularly on terraces and in entry/exit routes.

20. *Emergency evacuation:* The third type of safety problem cannot be divorced from the second and in some ways is an extreme version of it. The danger arises from emergency situations which can develop following, for example, an outbreak of crowd disorder or fire. The orderly evacuation of large crowds may, under emergency conditions, become a serious problem.

21. *Fire:* the fourth is the risk from fire, particularly where there is a large crowd in a confined area of an elevated covered stand where spectators are in the upper levels, the materials and construction of which might in themselves constitute a fire risk (see Chapter 13).

Overcoming the problems
22. *Good ground management:* The importance of good ground management cannot be emphasised too strongly (see Chapter 2). Much of this Guide contains advice on matters which should form part of the general upkeep and maintenance of a sports ground. If followed, it will reduce or eliminate risks to spectators and in the long term should prove cost effective by preventing serious defects. A well maintained and well-run venue makes commercial sense and may attract more events and a greater number of spectators.

23. *Improving safety by new design:* As mentioned in paragraph 11 above, new design work can provide an opportunity to enhance spectator safety and should be given the highest priority when deciding upon the design, layout, materials and loading of new buildings, or alterations in a ground. Close attention should be paid to new and existing exits and exit routes, slip-resistant surfaces, lighting and ease of maintenance. All parts of the viewing areas should always have a clear, unobstructed view of the playing area and designs should take account of the need to facilitate effective stewarding, which plays an important role in controlling crowd movement (see Chapter 16).

24. New design work also offers the chance to improve amenities and standards of comfort for spectators. Attention to decor, careful planning of catering or other refreshment areas can encourage spectators to arrive in good time, influence the use of different ingress and egress routes and may contribute towards improving crowd behaviour. Where segregation of spectators is a feature, special attention is needed in order to ensure a good standard of amenity is available in each segregated part of the ground.

25. *Care and maintenance:* Although controlling crowd numbers may serve to reduce some risks to an acceptable level, remedial work is likely to be necessary to overcome others. Obvious defects such as trip hazards (particularly at the head of stairs or steps), loose or weak handrails or guard-rails, and obstructed exits or exit routes, should be rectified as part of a continuous programme of remedial care and maintenance of a ground.

26. Structures should be sound (see Chapter 4) and inspected by suitably qualified persons (see Chapter 5). Design, layout and signposting of entrances, exits, entry and exit routes require particular attention so as to ensure that they can safely cope with the number of spectators who will use them (see Chapters 6 and 7). Attention should be paid to the condition of terraces, viewing slopes (see Chapter 9) and crush barriers (see Chapter 10). Broken, uneven terraces cause stumbling. Crush barriers serve to break up crowd pressures and help control movement from the terraces by regulating the rate of arrival at exits to suit their capacity, and encourage the formation of orderly queues.

27. *Fire precautions:* Proper precautions should be taken to minimise the risk of fire. Accumulation of litter is a prime potential source of fire but can be eliminated by regular, frequent inspections, good housekeeping, maintenance and safe provision over the care and storage of flammable materials. The nature and type of materials used in the construction of covered areas and stands will strongly influence the safety measures required in them.

2. MANAGEMENT RESPONSIBILITY

Effective ground management is an essential element in achieving safety. Management should constantly look to improve safety standards.

General Duty

28. The responsibility for the safety of spectators at the ground lies at all times with the ground management ie those who stage the event and/or administer the ground. Local authority safety officers, police and fire officers will advise management on how to discharge this responsibility and, in certain circumstances, may require measures to be taken in order to achieve reasonable safety standards. This does not, however, exonerate the ground management from its responsibility for the safety of spectators.

Safety Policy

29. As part of the drive for success of the club, team or individual event, senior management, directors and board members must devote time, effort and resources to safety management at the ground, both in its day to day use or for any special event. There should be a written policy of safety for spectators and employees covering the safety objectives and the means of achieving them. This should be known to and understood by all staff and voluntary workers who may be involved in ground operations. This policy should be kept under review by management and revised as necessary. Annex A summarises issues which should be addressed by the policy.

30. The management should require regular, periodic reports on safety measures taken and on progress on those in hand. They should ensure that they are made aware of details of any minor incidents (which might suggest underlying problems) and the action taken to rectify them. Such details should be kept in written form and, together with the policy statement on safety, should be available for inspection.

Safety Officer

31. There should be an appointed safety officer who should be of sufficient competence, status and authority effectively to take responsibility for safety at the ground and be able to authorise and supervise safety measures. The safety officer should be accountable to the most senior management or Board of Directors to whom the right of direct access is essential.

32. The safety officer or an appointed deputy should be in attendance at a central control point when an event takes place. The sole duty of that person during the course of the event should be that of safety, and he or she should be easily identifiable. All staff should know the location of the central control point, who is in charge of safety on the day in question and the line of communication.

33. A programme of checks, inspections, tests, training and remedial work should be drawn up so as to eliminate or minimise the potential risks to spectators. The safety officer should be responsible for ensuring that such inspections are carried out on all structures, installations and equipment so that they are safe and fit for the purpose for which they were intended. The details of any remedial work carried out including the dates of completion should be recorded. Adequate resources to carry out these tasks should be made available.

Emergency Plan

34. Plans should be made to deal with emergencies. Consultation between management, police, fire and ambulance services should take place in order to produce an agreed plan of action, including access for emergency vehicles, for all foreseeable incidents (see also paragraph 42 vi).

Staffing

35. While the public are in the ground management should ensure that sufficient staff are on duty to cover entrances, exits (including any emergency exits) and other strategic points or areas.

36. Staff training, particularly for stewards, in carrying out both their normal duties and ensuring that they are aware of their role in an emergency situation, should be given high priority. All staff should be capable of undertaking the duties allocated to them. They should be informed in writing what their duties are, how to effect them and from whom to seek advice if in doubt. These instructions should be available for inspection. The safety officer should also carry out active supervision and organise emergency drills to maintain standards (see Chapter 16).

Restrictions
37. Where restrictions on crowd numbers to parts of the ground are required for safety reasons they must be imposed and enforced. Similarly, if part of the ground is required to be closed, this must be done, and it must not be opened up for any reason unless measures have been taken beforehand to remove the dangers which led to its closure in the first place and approval given by the appropriate authority to re-open it.

Fire safety
38. Management should ensure that structural fire protection of buildings is adequate, and that fire warning systems are correctly installed and properly maintained in accordance with manufacturers' instructions or British Standards. Suitable fire-fighting equipment must be provided and maintained to the standards specified in this Guide (see Chapter 13).

First Aid Provision
39. A properly equipped and staffed First Aid room and suitable medical facilities should be provided in consultation with the local Health Authority's Chief Ambulance Officer (see Annex B).

Miscellaneous
40. Where a capacity or near capacity crowd is expected for an event, admission should normally be by ticket only.

41. General repair and maintenance should be undertaken with spectator safety in mind; litter should not be allowed to accumulate. Minor repairs should be quickly and properly carried out.

Summary of Management Responsibilities
42. A summary of management responsibilities is contained below:-

i. Appoint a safety officer.

ii. Where required, apply for and ensure compliance with the terms and conditions of a safety certificate or other notice covering the safety at the ground.

iii. Draw up and keep up to date plans of the ground; maintain the general fabric of the ground, and arrange an annual detailed inspection.

iv. Arrange an annual inspection of all crush barriers, handrails/guard-rails and ensure a representative sample are tested, (keeping a record of those tested and results of the tests).

v. Maintain and test all electrical installations for emergency lighting, communications and fire warning/detection, and fire-fighting equipment in accordance with the relevant British Standards and Codes of Practice.

vi. Prepare in conjunction with the police, fire and ambulance services contingency plans, including arrangements for stopping or delaying an event, for:

    a. various emergency situations including fire;
    b. possible crowd disturbance;
    c. coping with an exceptionally large number of spectators arriving at the ground; and
    d. the failure of any detection, warning, lighting or communications system or other equipment.

vii.   Devise a clear system of communications inside and outside the ground (including direct communication with any police control within the ground).

viii   Take necessary fire prevention and precautions measures.

ix.   Consult the fire authority about emergency evacuation, fire risk and provision of fire-fighting equipment.

x.   Consult the police, fire and ambulance services on access for emergency vehicles.

xi.   Store safely and away from public areas any flammable materials and any accumulations of combustible waste which cannot be cleared from the ground before the next event.

xii.   Provide first aid facilities and first aid staff.

xiii. Consult with the police to arrange adequate policing and police facilities and ensure that, where the police are to be present at the ground, there is a clear understanding of the division of duties and responsibility between them and the management.

xiv   Recruit, train and deploy stewards and organise and carry out emergency evacuation drills using those staff.

xv.   Staff exit gates at all times when the public are in the ground and ensure that such gates can be, and are, opened immediately from the inside in an emergency.

xvi.   Ensure that all gangways and exit routes are unobstructed and capable of being used to their full capacity at all times when the public are in the ground.

xvii. Provide directional flow, exit and emergency exit signs.

xviii. Before each event:

   a. test the operation of exit doors and gates;

   b. test lighting, communications and fire warning/detection systems;

   c. check the ground for any accumulations of combustible litter, especially below stands and in exit routes; and for any source of potential missiles;

   d. check security of any container used for storage of combustible material;

   e. check the operation of the turnstiles and metering system;

   f. check that all entry/exit routes are clear of obstruction;

   g. ensure that there are sufficient stewards for the event and inform the police ground commander before the ground is open to the public.

xix.   After each event:

   a. carry out a general visual inspection for signs of damage;

   b. liaise with police so as to gain full benefit from any debriefing about crowd control.

xx.   Keep records of:

   a. attendance figures;

   b. all inspections and tests, any defects noted and the remedial/other action taken;

   c. any accident or reported incident which might have led to an accident;

   d. staff training and emergency evacuation drills.

43. The management should ensure that details of all consultations, arrangements, plans between them and the police, fire and ambulance services are notified to the relevant local authority if there is a safety certificate issued in respect of the ground or stand(s) within the ground.

3. SPECTATORS WITH DISABILITIES

Proper provision to accommodate safely people with disabilities should be made at all grounds.

General
44. The safety measures set out in the Guide should not be construed in such a way as to place undue restrictions on people with disabilities.

People with impaired vision
45. Signposting (see paragraphs 84 and 101) especially fire or other safety signs, should be sited so that as far as possible they can be easily seen and readily distinguishable by those with impaired vision or colour perception. Advice is available from the Royal National Institute for the Blind or the National Federation of the Blind of the UK.

People with impaired hearing
46. Although people with impaired hearing may experience difficulty in hearing messages broadcast on a system designed for those with normal hearing (see Chapter 14) a hearing impairment does not mean that in all cases a person is insensitive to sound and that they do not have a sufficiently clear perception of all conventional alarm signals. Where this is not the case it is reasonable to expect spectators who have been alerted to prepare for evacuation to warn those with impaired hearing.

47. Where they exist, electronic score boards and television and television monitors should be used to give information on evacuation.

People with impaired mobility
48. Although it is unlikely that anyone whose mobility is severely impaired will occupy standing accommodation they will often wish to occupy seated accommodation, perhaps with friends or relatives, in stands. Arrangements should therefore exist to meet such wishes wherever it is possible to do so, for example by the provision of wheelchair spaces within the seated area, preferably in different parts so that there is a choice of seating position. Such provision should take account of the sightlines available from the allocated areas to ensure that occupants have an unrestricted view.

49. Wherever possible there should be more than one ingress/egress for those with impaired mobility. Although movement to and from accommodation at ground level is easier for users of wheelchairs, consideration should be given to the means by which they can be accommodated on other levels without prejudicing their safety or the safety of others.

Wheelchairs
50. Where a person leaves a wheelchair in order to occupy a seat, provision should be made for the wheelchair to be readily accessible without it causing an obstruction in a gangway or exit route. Those who remain in a wheelchair should be accommodated so as not to obstruct the movement of others.

Support Facilities
51. Ramps which are to be used by wheelchair users should conform to BS 5810.

52. Support services and facilities for disabled people should also be available within the stand.

53. New design work for stands should take account of guidance in BS 5588 Part 8 (Code of Practice for means of escape for disabled people). Where, because of constraints posed by existing buildings, it is not possible or practicable to apply the Code fully, alternative ways of meeting its objectives should be sought.

54. The arrangements described above should be in addition to any special provision made for the admission (often at pitch level) of vehicles used by people with impaired mobility. The location of such vehicles should be agreed with the relevant safety authority in order to ensure that access to the ground by emergency vehicles and means of escape are not compromised.

Use of lifts in an emergency
55. A lift should be used as a means of escape from a stand only if it is an evacuation lift or firefighting lift operated under the direction and control of an appointed steward designated with specific responsibility for its use in an evacuation using an agreed evacuation procedure. BS 5588 Part 8 recommendations, which specify the facilities that need to be incorporated in an evacuation lift, should be followed.

4. GENERAL FABRIC AND STRUCTURAL MATTERS

All components, installations and structures such as terraces, stands, stairs, barriers and pylons, should have the strength, durability, and should be maintained in such condition and arranged in such a manner as to perform properly their required functions.

General

56. The design and construction of buildings and installations should be in accordance with good engineering and building practice, as set out in the relevant British Standard specifications and codes of practice. They should be properly maintained and repaired by suitably qualified persons. Specialist advice from appropriately qualified engineers belonging to a recognised Institution should be sought to assess the safety and strength of load-bearing elements in buildings and installations such as crush barriers, (see Chapter 10) brick/block walls etc (see Chapter 9, paragraph 157).

57. Walls, including boundary walls, and fences which are to withstand crowd pressures, should be designed and maintained to withstand such pressures safely. Allowance should be made for forces simultaneously and independently induced by other factors eg wind forces or attached installations.

Headroom

58. All parts of the ground used by the general public should have minimum headroom of not less than 2 metres. Exit routes should wherever possible have a headroom of 2.4 metres.

59. Precautions should be taken to prevent people from climbing on to roofs, pylons, hoardings and other structures. Where possible such structures should be fitted with unclimbable devices eg stout barriers or close-boarded enclosures. Spikes, barbed wire etc should only be installed above the minimum headroom specified in paragraph 58 above and preferably at a minimum height of 2.4 metres from the base. Spikes or other similar devices should not be installed on pitch perimeter fences. Nor should such fences have sections overhanging or returning inwards towards spectators (see Chapter 18).

Electrical installation

60. All electrical installations should comply with the Electricity at Work Regulations 1989 and also with the Electricity Supply Regulations 1988. New electrical installations should also comply with the edition of the Wiring Regulations of the Institution of Electrical Engineers (IEE) current at the date of installation. The IEE Completion Certificate as prescribed for electrical installations in the IEE Regulations should be retained by the proprietor of the ground.

61. The installation should be regularly inspected and an IEE Inspection Certificate as prescribed in the IEE regulations should be obtained. The interval between inspections should be no longer than five years, and necessary repairs promptly carried out.

62. A diagram of the main electrical circuit should be fixed in a position easily accessible to the technical staff. All main switches or circuit breakers should be clearly labelled to indicate the circuits which they control.

63. All cables and conductors of wiring systems should be sited so that they are, as far as practicable, inaccessible to the public and should be enclosed throughout in a protective covering of material which has sufficient strength to resist mechanical damage - for example armoured cables, sheathed cables protected by screwed metal conduit, trunking complying with BS 4678 Part 1 or Part 4, or rigid PVC conduit complying with relevant British Standards. PVC conduit should not be used in confined areas because of fire smoke hazard.

64. The base of any floodlighting tower should be earthed in accordance with BS 6651 which also contains advice on bonding and earthing for lightning protection.

Lighting

65. Where the natural lighting in any section of the ground accessible to the public is deficient, adequate artificial lighting should be provided. If the ground is to be used after dark, all parts accessible to the public should be provided with means for lighting adequate to enable them to see their way into, within and out of the ground. These provisions are particularly important in relation to entry and exit routes and stairways used by the public. Emergency lighting should be provided and conform to BS 5266: Part 1 (see Chapter 15).

5. INSPECTIONS AND TESTS

Inspections and tests should be carried out by suitably qualified persons on behalf of the management to ensure that the safety standards are maintained.

Annual Inspection

66. A detailed inspection of the ground, including all components and installations, should be arranged annually by the management in order to ensure that load-bearing elements are capable of withstanding the pressures to which they are likely to be subjected and that they are fit for their intended purpose (see also paragraphs 56-57). Inspection should be carried out by a person with a relevant, recognised professional qualification, and with experience of inspecting structures.

67. Engineers commissioned to assess structural safety of buildings may find the appraisal techniques recommended by the Institution of Structural Engineers (ISE) in the "Appraisal of Existing Structures" of assistance. Hard and fast rules on the extent to which a structural appraisal is necessary for individual buildings are difficult to lay down: much will depend upon the type of installation, its size, condition, materials used in construction and standard of maintenance. A full appraisal is unlikely to be necessary unless defects are identified or in evidence from the analysis of information on the structure and visual inspection.

68. Inspection and testing of crush barriers, handrails and other protective barriers should be carried out in accordance with Chapter 10 and Annex D of this Guide.

Other inspections

69. Warning, detection, lighting and public address systems are vulnerable to vandalism, and this should be borne in mind when installing them. All automatic fire detection and fire warning, emergency lighting and public address systems should be tested 24 hours before an event, in accordance with the methods laid down in BS 5839: Part 1 and BS 5266: Part 1 respectively.

70. Turnstiles and metering systems should be tested before each event in order to ensure that they are in proper working order.

71. There should be contingency plans in case any of these systems is not operating properly and cannot be rectified before the event. Such plans should be formulated, in consultation with the local authority (if a safety certificate is in force), police and fire services, for the use of acceptable substitute measures or (if necessary) the closure of relevant areas of spectator accommodation until the fault is remedied.

72. Before an event, and at major soccer grounds in particular, steps should be taken to ensure that the ground does not contain any accessible items which could be used as missiles.

73. The ground should be inspected before, during and after each event to ensure that there are no accumulations of combustible waste and that any hazardous materials (if essential to be stored) are safely stored well away from public areas.

Deformation/Damage

74. Following each event, a general visual inspection of the ground should be made for signs of damage which might create a potential danger to the public. Particular attention should be paid to the condition of terraces, viewing slopes and stairways. Crush barriers and balustrades should be examined for deformation or any other overt signs of weakness. The fire precautions measures should also be inspected for damage. Alarm and other electrical installations should be checked to ensure continued compliance with the relevant British Standards. Turnstiles should be checked for damage which might impair their efficiency.

Records

75. Records should be kept and maintained of all inspections and tests together with a record of remedial actions taken. The required level of competence of those carrying out the test should be specified and the record of the results certified by those carrying out the work together with their qualification and status.

76. Annex C provides a tabulation of tests and inspections and their frequency of operation.

6. INGRESS

Spectators entering the ground should be accurately counted and their number controlled in order to ensure that overcrowding does not occur. Spectators should be admitted at a rate which is compatible with the dispersal arrangements for them inside the ground.

Turnstiles

77. The number and location of turnstiles control not only the rate of admission but, to a large extent, the dispersal of spectators within a ground to the particular sections. Sufficient turnstiles should therefore be provided in order to admit spectators at a rate whereby no unduly large crowds are kept waiting for admission and yet at no faster rate than the arrangements for distributing spectators within the ground permit.

78. Each section of viewing accommodation should be served by its own metered turnstiles which keep a tally of the number of spectators admitted to that section. Where a section is served by a bank or banks of turnstiles, arrangements must ensure that the metering system is capable of recording the total of all the turnstiles for that section. The total should be quickly available at any given time so that appropriate action can be taken once a pre-determined figure (ie a figure which is less than the capacity for the section) has been reached. This is especially important if a capacity or near capacity crowd is expected or if a particular section of a ground is known to be popular or likely to accommodate an unusually high number of spectators for a particular event.

79. The correlation between each section of the viewing accommodation in the ground and the turnstiles serving it should be such as to ensure that all spectators intended to be admitted to that accommodation and who are to pass through the turnstiles can do so within one hour. If that cannot be achieved, the capacity of that viewing accommodation in that part of the ground should be reduced accordingly, or the number of turnstiles increased (see also Chapter 19).

80. The maximum rate at which spectators can pass through turnstiles will depend on a variety of factors such as the design and age of the equipment, the ability of the operator and the ticketing arrangements. The rate of admission at each turnstile will therefore depend greatly upon local circumstances. The through-put or flow-rate through turnstiles should therefore be measured at least once a year and recorded. Where a recorded flow-rate is less than 660 persons per turnstile per hour the actual figure should be used for calculation purposes of paragraph 79 above. The maximum upper figure for calculation purposes should not exceed 660 persons per hour.

Computer Monitoring

81. Centralised computer monitoring should be installed wherever practicable and at all grounds in the 1st and 2nd Division of the English Football League, Premier Division of the Scottish Football League and grounds used for international or other major sporting events.

Entrances and Entry Routes

82. Entry and exit routes are often common to each other and in such cases the considerations which apply to exit routes therefore apply also to entry routes (see paragraphs 91-96 of Chapter 7). These routes should not be obstructed. Amenities such as refreshment kiosks or toilets should be located away from the area of the turnstiles, entrances and entry/exit routes.

83. Entrances to each part of the ground should, where practicable, be designed and located so as to allow for the even distribution of spectators and to prevent local pressure building up outside the ground. They should be sited so that the flow of people from them is, as far as possible, evenly distributed to the viewing accommodation. Where this distribution is uneven and gives rise to congestion at an entrance consideration will have to be given to changing the turnstile arrangements or siting in order to encourage better use of under-used entrances. Additional or alternative measures should also be taken: for example improved sign-posting and increased stewarding either inside or outside the ground.

Signposting

84. Clear, comprehensive signposting should be provided in order to show the routes to different parts of the ground. Tickets (where issued) should clearly identify the location of the accommodation for which they have been issued. Information on the ticket should correlate with the information provided both inside and outside the ground. Colour coding of tickets should be considered and retained ticket stubs should contain information which will help guide spectators once they are inside the ground. Large scale wall maps showing location should also be considered.

Programmes

85. Where possible, programmes should include a plan of the ground indicating the entry/exit routes to or from different parts of the ground and their destination.

Crowd Build-Up

86. Dangerous overcrowding can be caused if spectators are able to force their way into a ground already full or nearly full by scaling or breaking through boundary walls or fences or the gates in them. To avoid this danger such walls, fences and gates should be of appropriate height and strength and should not provide the opportunity for hand or foot holds which might assist climbing. They should be regularly inspected.

87. Installation of closed circuit television should be considered in order to assist in the monitoring of crowd densities outside the ground and throughout the ingress/egress routes (see paragraph 264 Chapter 14).

88. Contingency plans should be drawn up with the police in order to deal with situations where unduly large crowds have gathered outside. Local knowledge of the ground and crowd patterns should be taken into account in drawing up contingency plans. Opening additional or under-used entrances may have to be considered. However, under no circumstances should there be uncontrolled admission into the ground.

7. EGRESS

There should be a smooth, unimpeded passage through an exit route and a free flow of people from one element to the next until they reach the boundary of the ground.

89. It is generally recognised that a period of great risk to crowd safety is at the time of leaving. Pressures can be set up within a departing crowd; such pressures can and must be contained and controlled by careful attention to the detailed design of barriers (Chapter 10), stairways (Chapter 8), gangways (Chapter 9) and exits.

90. Additional consideration which must be given to egress from covered stands and seated accommodation is given in paragraphs 177-179 of Chapter 11.

Exit Routes/Systems

91. A smooth free flow through an exit route to the outside is best achieved by controlling the crowd flow at the beginning of it, so that departing spectators are held back in a relatively safe place, for example on viewing accommodation, enabling access to the exit route at a calculated rate. That is to say the capacity of the first element of the exit route from the viewing accommodation should be no greater than any subsequent element. The exit route will then be able to accommodate throughout its length and discharge spectators at a rate compatible with that at which they enter into the route.

92. If there is any deviation from the recommended guidelines which creates a potential danger, that section should be closed. Until remedial action has been taken, a reduction should be made accordingly in the spectator capacity of the section of the ground it serves; ie the exit route is excluded from the capacity calculations.

93. The minimum width of an exit route should be 1.1 metres. If any part of an exit route is less than 1 metre wide that route should be excluded from the exit capacity calculations. For capacities of exit routes see Chapter 19, paragraphs 326-330.

94. Exit systems should ensure that in the event of an incident which blocks the usual exit route spectators will be able to use an alternative exit route or routes. In appropriate cases forward evacuation on to the pitch can form part of the emergency evacuation route (see Chapter 13 paragraph 236).

95. There should be no "funnelling" effect causing people to converge on a narrower means of access or egress. This will slow down the rate at which people can pass through the entire exit system and cause them to pack more closely together. However a narrowing in the exit route may be acceptable when it is preceded by an open space or "reservoir area" where the holding capacity is sufficient to contain the spectators held up because of the difference in the flow rate into and out of the reservoir area (but see also paragraph 96 below). The capacity of the reservoir areas should be calculated using the appropriate flow rate given in Chapter 20 and the recommended exit time given in paragraph 97 below. A packing density of **40 persons per 10 square metres** of the area available for standing within the reservoir area **is the maximum for safety**. Arrangements should be such as to prevent this being exceeded.

96. Reservoir areas should be avoided wherever possible and should not be permitted within 45 metres of any combustible building within the ground eg a timber stand, or within 15 metres of any non-combustible building within the ground.

Egress time

97. Crowd flow tends to become turbulent when it takes more than about 7 minutes to vacate an area of terraced spectator accommodation. In these conditions the rate of flow may be reduced and individuals can lose control over their own movements which may increase the potential for accidents. Sufficient exits from each section of viewing accommodation should be provided so that all spectators can leave that area and pass into a free flowing exit route system within 8 minutes or less. This applies to both standing and seated areas even though spectators normally vacate seated accommodation in a more leisurely fashion.

98. Once spectators have passed into the exit system they should be able to move at the same speed throughout its length. Calculation of exit capacity is shown in Chapter 19, paragraphs 326-330, using the maximum recommended flow rates given in Chapter 20.

99. The exit routes available for use by spectators in an emergency are in many instances the same as those used by them in normal circumstances - for example from the upper tiers of a stand. If the capacity of the exit routes is considered insufficient for evacuation purposes the number of spectators occupying the accommodation will have to reflect that exit route capacity.

100. In some cases exit routes, not normally used by spectators, may be made available for them where the playing area or perimeter track is used as part of the emergency evacuation route but does not form part of the normal egress route. In such circumstances there should be a route from the playing area or perimeter track to an exit from the ground.

Signposting
101. A comprehensive system of signposting which clearly indicates routes to the various parts of the ground, and to exits from the ground, should be provided. Signs relating to fire safety should be in accordance with BS 5499: Part 1 and other safety signs should be in accordance with BS 5378: Part 1. Exit gates themselves should be clearly signposted, preferably using illuminated signs in accordance with BS 5499: Part 2 or Part 3. Directional signs should be provided to encourage crowds in any particular section to flow in one direction when leaving the ground and should, wherever practicable, provide information on the destination of the exit route (eg north side car-park, High Street) so as to provide confidence to people using them, especially if they are evacuating the premises.

Exit routes
102. Exit routes should be kept clear of obstructions. In particular, no catering, sales or toilet facility should be situated in such a way that it, or any queue it attracts, obstructs an exit route.

103. Where there is a simple exit route, ie a direct passage from the accommodation area to the exit gate from the ground, every part of that route should be able to accommodate the flow from the terrace or stand exit.

104. For a more complex exit system which combines a number of exit routes and/or offers a choice of alternative routes to exits, the system should be analysed in the form of a network in order to check that the capacity of the exit from the terrace or the stand is sufficient to ensure a free flow of spectators to the various exits from the ground. Where branching of routes gives spectators a choice of paths, the proportion of the crowd likely to use each path should be derived from local knowledge, eg the exit closest to a railway or bus station may be likely to attract a higher proportion of spectators.

105. Grounds which have complex exit systems should have illustrative plans of the network system which serves each section, identifying the capacity of the routes within the system and clearly showing them on the plans. These plans should be kept with the drawings of the section of the ground to which they relate. Any changes to the ground which affect the entry/exit routes should be identified on the network plan. An example of a network plan is given in Figures 1.1 and 1.2. Other examples are contained in Chapter 19.

Figure 1.1
Exit systems leading from enclosure and stand

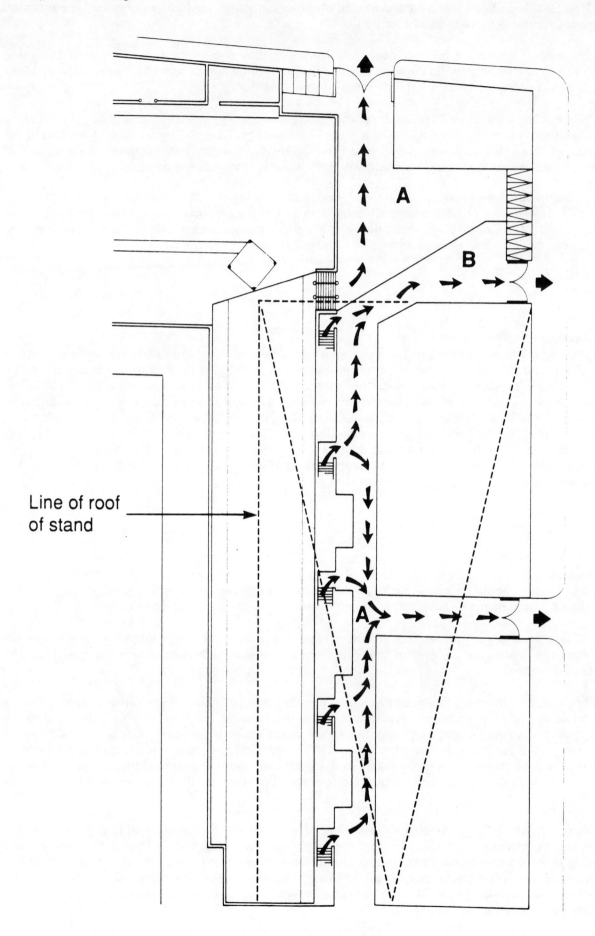

Line of roof of stand

A

B

A

Figure 1.2
Exit Systems A and B represented on a network plan
Each element within the network should be analysed in order to assess the exit capacity. (See Chapter 19).

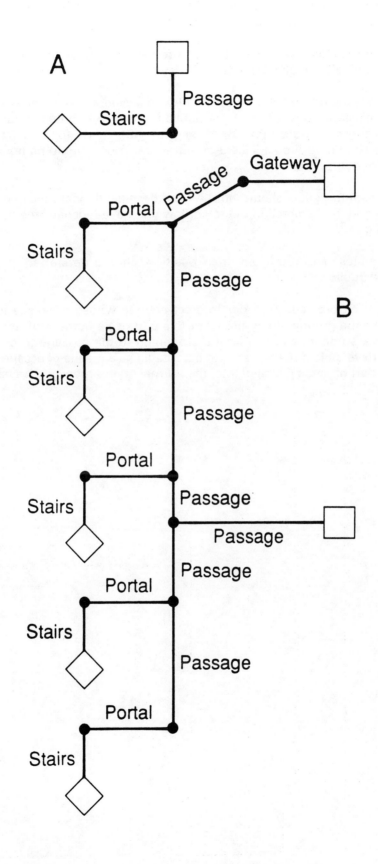

Exit doors and Gates

106. No door or gate forming part of an escape route should be locked or fastened in such a way that it cannot easily and immediately be opened by those using that route in an emergency.

107. All exit doors on an exit route should always be capable of opening outwards so that crowds can escape in an emergency without obstruction. This is particularly important for doors within covered stands and at the foot of stairways.

108. All doors on a normal exit route should be secured in the fully open position before the end of play. When open, no door should obstruct any gangway passage, stairway or landing.

109. All exit gates from the ground should open outwards. Where this is impracticable, for example because they would cause an obstruction on a public highway, the gates should be resited (ie put further back) within the exit route they serve, or provision made for two-way opening. Where practicable exit gates should be sited adjacent to entrances. There should be no obstructions and no changes in level at exit doors.

110. Sliding or roller-shutter gates should not be used because they are incapable of being opened when pressure is exerted in the direction of crowd flow and have mechanisms or runways which are vulnerable to jamming.

111. All exit gates, unless secured in an open position, should be staffed at all times while the ground is used by the public.

112. Facilities should be provided in order to eject anyone whose presence is unwanted and to enable people to leave the ground at any time. For this purpose a number of reversible turnstiles or, preferably, pass doors, so operated as to limit the opening to the passage to one person at a time, should be provided. Reversible turnstiles are not acceptable as a means of escape from a ground and should not form any part of, or be installed into, the normal or emergency exit system of the ground.

8. STAIRWAYS AND RAMPS

The disposition and construction of stairways and ramps should be such as to help provide a smooth and unimpeded ingress and egress for spectators under all conditions set out in Chapters 6 and 7.

113. For the purpose of this section the term "stairway" has the meaning given to it in the Glossary (Annex F) and is distinct from a radial gangway on a terrace or in a stand. Guidelines on terrace gangways is given in Chapter 9, paragraphs 143-151 and for stands in Chapter 11, paragraphs 180-182.

114. Movement on stairways, especially downwards, poses a considerable potential risk to crowds both in normal circumstances such as at the end of an event, or in an emergency. The effects of stumbling, pushing, jostling, and congestion are potentially dangerous if, as a result, the crowd suddenly surges forward. Similarly, if sections of the crowd decide, without warning, to change direction the resultant turmoil can have serious consequences. Steep ramps can cause or exacerbate uncontrolled forward movement and lead to an accident.

115. Stairways should, therefore, minimise hazards by having uniformity of width, going and risers, secure footing and a suitable gradient. They should be wide enough to allow free movement but also provide, as far as possible, everyone with access to a handrail. The head of the stairway should be so designed that flow onto it is uniform across its width and so that crowd pressures cannot easily be generated. Flights should not provide long, uncontrolled paths down which crowd pressures and surges can be created. Adequate separation should be provided between channels so that there is no overspill from one channel to another.

Disposition of stairways

116. Stairways should be carefully positioned to take advantage of natural light and ventilation. Where the natural lighting is deficient the stairway should be adequately lit by artificial light (see Chapter 4, paragraph 65 and Chapter 15, paragraphs 269-272 for emergency lighting).

Construction of stairways

117. The width, rise and going of the steps should be uniform within each stairway, and, ideally, should be uniform throughout the entire exit system.

118. Stair treads should be provided with slip-resistant surfaces and durable edgings. Adequate drainage should be provided.

119. Open risers should not be used.

120. On any stairway the preferred going of treads should be 305 mm but not less than 280 mm; and preferred height of risers should be 150 mm but not more than 190 mm. Stairways should:

    i.   be without winders;

    ii.   be in flights of not more than 16; and

    iii.   make at least one change in direction between flights of at least 30° if there are more than 36 risers in consecutive flights.

121. The going of the landing between flights should not be less than the width of the channel of the flight.

122. Guarding should be provided on both sides of all stairs and landings. Where next to open wells, or spaces, such guarding should conform to Building Regulation requirements but should be not less than 1.1 metres in height (measured vertically from the nosing of the step, or the surface of the landing). The guarding should have a strength equivalent to that of the crush barriers of the weaker type, described in Chapter 10. (ie 3.4 kN/metre width design force, 4.1 kN/metre width test load.)

123. The minimum width of a stairway or stairway channel should be 1.1 metres. The maximum width of a stairway channel should be 1.65 metres. Consideration will have to be given to dividing existing stairways wider than 1.65 metres but which do not exceed 2.2 metres taking account of the extent to which they comply with the other stairway requirements of the Guide. Stairways of 2.2 metres or more should be divided into channels having a width of between 1.1 metres and 1.65 metres (see examples at Figures 2-4).

124. Handrails should project not more than 100 mm and should be provided on both sides of all stairways, steps and landings at a height of not less than 840 mm (measured vertically from the line of the step nosing or the surface of the landing). All handrails should extend by at least 300 mm beyond the top and bottom of any ramp or risers of the staircase.

125. The strength of the handrails (including supports) used to divide a stairway into channels should be as described in Chapter 10, i.e. 3.4 kN/metre width design force or 4.1 kN/metre width test load for handrails at right angles to the direction of the crowd flow; 2.2 kN/metre width design force or 2.7 kN/metre width test load for handrails parallel to the direction of the flow.

Figure 2
1.525 metre staircase

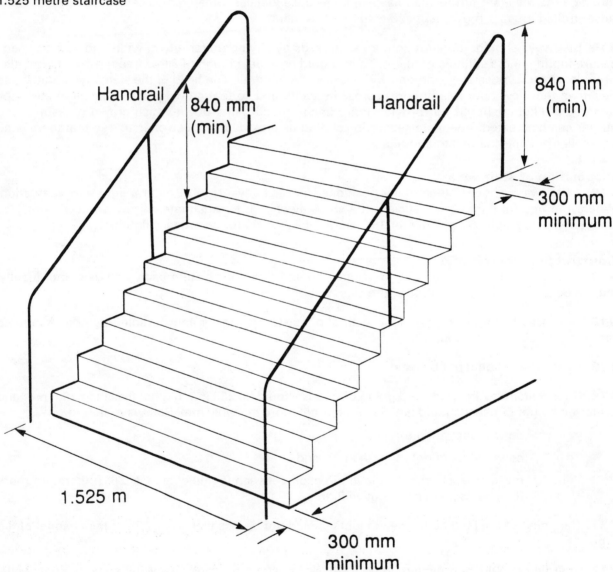

Notes
No centre rail considered desirable because stairway width is under 1.65 metres.
Handrails at each side should extend at least 300mm beyond the top and bottom risers of the stairways.
Flow rate calculation reflects actual width:-

$$\frac{1.525}{.55} \text{ m} \times 40 = 111 \text{ per minute}$$

Figure 3.
2.135 metre staircase

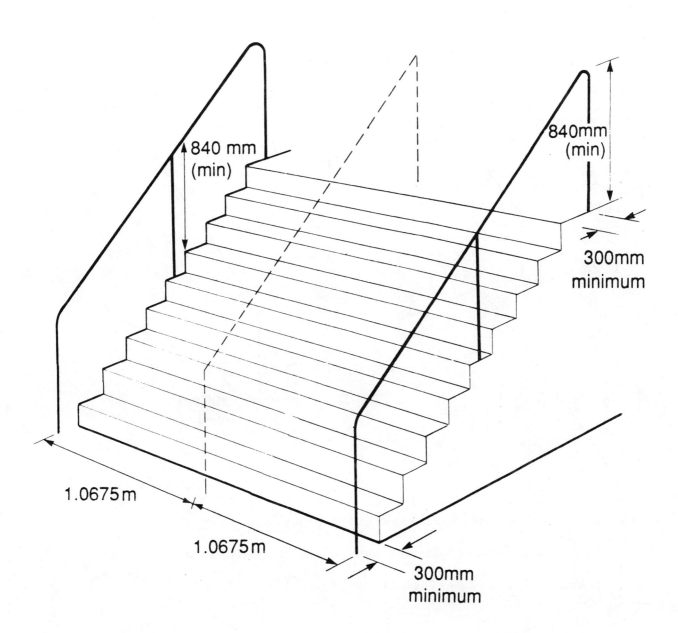

Notes

Consideration is given here to the option of dividing the staircase into two sections of 1.0675 metres or accepting it as a single channel stairway. Division would mean that each channel would be less than the recommended minimum of 1.1 metres but in certain circumstances may be judged preferable to having no centre rail at all. Factors to take into consideration would include use of staircase (ie. whether or not heavily loaded) its length, number or risers and landings, number of winders.

Handrails should extend at least 300mm beyond the top and bottom risers of the stairways.

Flow rate calculation $\frac{1.0675}{.55} \times 40 \times 2 = 155$ per minute

Figure 4.
3.66 metre staircase

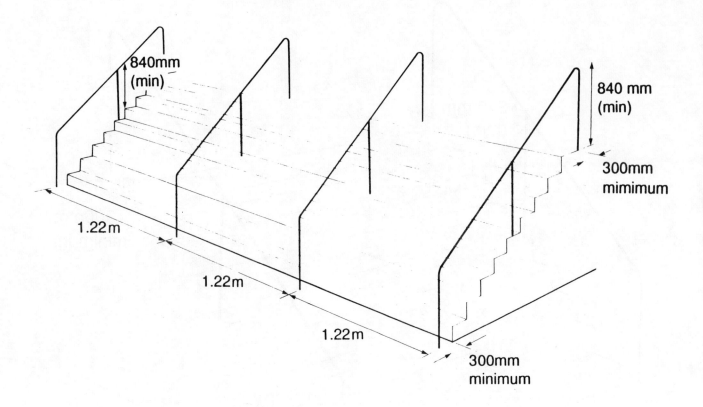

A 3.66 metre staircase divided into 3 channels of 1.22 metres each.

Handrails should extend at least 300mm beyond the top and bottom risers of the staircase.

Flow rate calculation $\frac{1.22}{.55} \times 40 \times 3 = 266$ per minute.

Access to stairways

126. Access to the head of the stairways should be controlled to ensure a free flow of spectators.

127. Where a stairway is divided into channels the access should be designed to secure a uniform flow down each channel.

128. The approach to the head of the stairs should be level and should be so arranged that the spectators converge on the stairway from the front and/or the sides only.

129. The approach in the direction of the stairway should not be less than 1.1 metres and preferably not more than 3 metres unless access is totally controlled, see Figure 5.

28

Figure 5.
Example of an approach to the head of a staircase

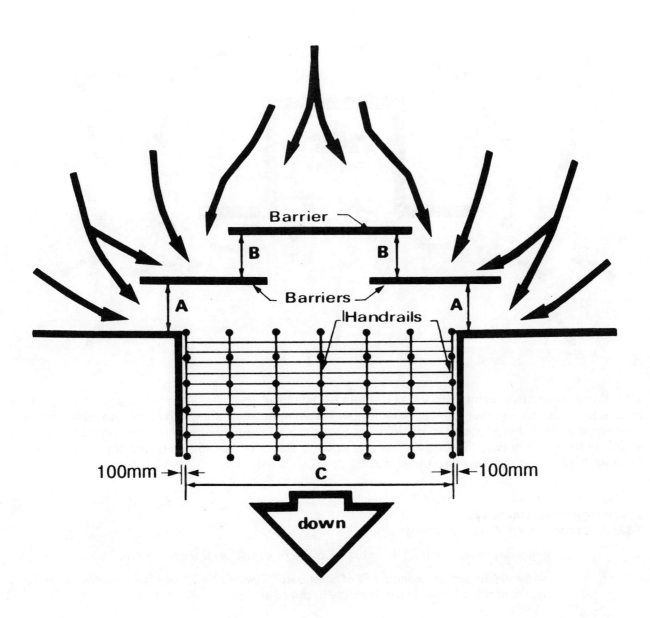

The width of A and B to be not less than 1.1m.

The aggregate width of A = B to be not more than 3m
$2(A+B) = \frac{2}{3} C$

The capacity of this stairway would be calculated from the width C.

130. There should be no approach from behind, involving movement around the ends of the balustrades or side walls of the stairway, except where this approach is already controlled by physical means such as by the gangways in the seated areas of the stand, see Figure 6.

Figure 6.
Exits attracting spectators from higher up the terrace should be protected by barriers so that spectators are forced to pass around them and approach from the side.

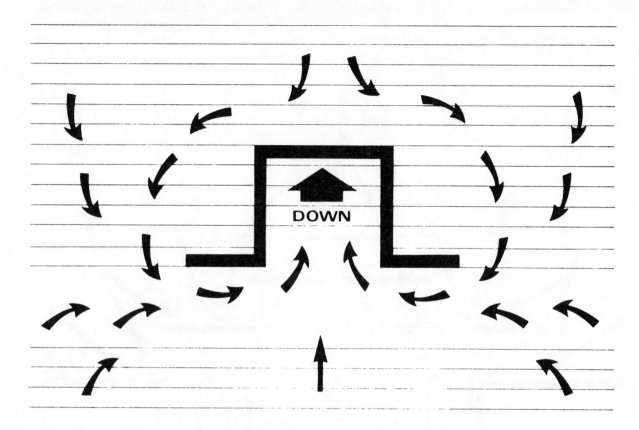

131. Where restrictive elements such as barriers or gateways are installed in the approach from the terrace to a stairway in order to meet the foregoing provisions, the total width of the passage formed by these elements should not be more than two-thirds the minimum width of the stairway, see Figure 5. This is to accommodate the slower flow rate down a staircase as compared with the flow rate on flat areas and through portals (see Chapter 20).

Discharge from stairways
132. All exit stairways should discharge either:

    i.   at ground level and lead directly to a place of safety* in the open air; or

    ii.   on to walkways or concourses of adequate dimensions at any level provided these also lead directly to a place of safety in the open air.

* In Scotland 'place of safety' is a defined term in the Scottish Building Regulations.

Fire Protection
133. This is dealt with in Chapter 13, paragraphs 238-240.

Ramps
134. The gradient should preferably be constant and not broken by steps.

135. The maximum gradient acceptable should not exceed 1 in 10.

136. Ramps installed for wheelchair users should conform to BS 5810 (see also Chapter 3 on provision for people with disabilities).

9. TERRACES AND VIEWING SLOPES

Arrangements should be made to encourage the even distribution of the crowd; to provide ease of ingress and egress; to control and facilitate movement, particularly if a local emergency should arise during the event; and to prevent the build up of pressures from reaching dangerous proportions.

General

137. Terraces are recognised as presenting a special safety problem especially at football grounds. The following guidance is therefore aimed mainly at football stadia but can be applied to any ground where standing terraces or viewing slopes are used for accommodating spectators.

138. In addition to the incidental dangers of standing for long periods on steep, terraced slopes, crowds may be subject to excessive pressures generated by spectators straining to see the event, by excitement, or by surging. Failure to provide spectators with an unobstructed view can cause them to stretch and strain.

Terrace steps

139. A terrace step should not be less than 280 mm or more than 380 mm wide. The preferred dimension is between 355 mm and 380 mm.

140. The height of risers should be between 75 mm and 180 mm. 75 mm is related to the minimum width of 280 mm. If the riser height is greater than 180mm, a crush barrier should be provided at the top of the riser.

141. Excessive variations in the gradient of a terrace should be avoided. Gradients steeper than 1 in 2 can be potentially dangerous. Where unavoidable, consideration should be given to reducing the number of spectators occupying that area or provision of additional crush barriers.

142. The surface of terrace steps should be even and of a slip-resistant material. Drainage should be provided to prevent rainwater causing deterioration.

Gangways

143. For the purpose of this section the term 'radial gangway' has the meaning given to it in the Glossary, Annex F.

144. Gangways, both radial and lateral are the means by which spectators are channelled in an orderly way into and out of the viewing areas. Siting of gangways, crush barriers (see Chapter 10), barriers governing the flow at the head of stairways and handrails dividing stairways (see Chapter 8) should be designed to provide a uniform flow of spectators to each of the exits from the viewing area.

145. All gangways should be even and free from trip hazards. Surfaces should be slip resistant. They should be painted with a non-slip paint in a conspicuous colour.

146. Spectators should be informed by signs and other means (for example in programmes and by the public address system) that no standing is allowed in gangways (see Chapter 2 paragraph 42(xvi)). Where necessary stewards should be used to enforce the instruction.

147. All spectators on the terraces should be within 12 metres of a gangway or exit as measured along a line of unobstructed travel from the viewing position, so that they can move quickly into the exit system. This may be achieved by a pattern of gangways (not less than 1.1 metres wide) linked to the exit system.

Lateral Gangways

148. Spectators should not be allowed to stand in lateral gangways because this disrupts the free movement along them and may obstruct the view of those on the terrace steps behind causing them to stretch and strain (see paragraph 138 above). Standing in the gangways will be discouraged if they are sunk approximately 150 mm and if crush barriers are provided behind but not immediately in front of them.

Radial Gangways

149. Movement on radial gangways is disrupted by the presence of spectators using them to view the activity on the playing area. Such gangways are often relatively long, downward paths through terraces and spectators standing in them are not protected by crush barriers in the event of a sudden movement forward. Radial gangways should therefore be kept clear. It may be helpful to sink them approximately 150 mm and to interrupt an otherwise continuously descending gangway by turns along lateral gangways.

150. Any balustrading wall, fence or gate at the foot of radial gangways should be of the same height as crush barriers and should be as strong as those of the stronger type, ie, 5.0 kN/metre width design force, or 6.0 kN/metre width test load (see also Chapter 10).

151. Radial gangways should not contain winders. Where the gangway is stepped the going should be uniform and the step dimensions should be compatible with those for the terrace which they serve (see paragraphs 139-140 above).

Division of spectator accommodation

152. A ground should be divided in order to prevent migrations by spectators which might cause dangerous overcrowding. Each division must have its own limit of safe capacity and be served by turnstiles or other arrangements which keep a tally of the number of people admitted. Each division of a ground, for example each end or side, should be self-contained with its own entrances, exits and toilet/refreshment facilities. Consideration should be given to providing suitable access from one division to another for use in an emergency but such access will not normally be taken into account in any exit capacity calculations.

153. Each of the divisions should be subdivided by such means as crush barriers and gangways, arranged so as to minimise the sway and surge of spectators and to discourage lateral movement. If a terrace or viewing slope is sub-divided into sections by structural means such as fences or railings, arrangements at the ground must be such as to ensure that these sub-divisions cannot be filled beyond their safe limit. This means, in effect, that they will need to be self contained sections or divisions of viewing accommodation (see also Chapter 17 paragraph 289).

154. At sporting events such as greyhound racing spectators may need to move freely within each division of the viewing accommodation as well as to and from amenity areas. This should be borne in mind when considering the need for division of the ground. Other sports, including Rugby Union and Rugby League, also frequently allow more freedom of movement for spectators. The advantage of this arrangement is that it provides spectators with an opportunity to disperse in a way which avoids concentrations of the crowd.

155. Grounds may still have their popular areas. Considerable care is therefore needed to ensure that any concentration of spectators does not exceed the safe capacity for the particular area in question. Well trained stewards should be provided to check, monitor and marshall spectators at such grounds.

156. In cases where mobility of spectators is a feature of the event, overall calculated packing density for standing should be below the maximum of 47 persons per 10 square metres in order for spectators to move in the way desired.

157. Railings, fences etc dividing sections of the ground should be of the strength of the crush barriers. Brick/block and similar solid structures lacking sufficient mass or tensile strength are poorly suited to withstand horizontal pressures, and where used to divide spectator accommodation, should be subject to regular structural appraisal by appropriately qualified persons (see Chapter 4) in order to ensure they are fit for their intended purpose (see Chapter 5, paragraph 66).

Crush barriers
158. Detailed advice on crush barriers is given in Chapter 10.

Viewing slopes (ie non-stepped sloping areas providing standing accommodation for spectators)
159. The surface of this form of standing accommodation should be covered with a slip- resistant material and should be even and properly drained.

160. The desirable maximum gradient for a viewing slope is 1 in 6 (ie 9.5 degrees). Note: this is different to the stepped terraced gradient quoted in paragraph 141 above. Viewing slopes with any steeper gradient should have continuous crush barriers between radial gangways.

161. The spacing of crush barriers should be the same as for those on terracing (see Chapter 10).

Terrace to touchline distance.
162. The minimum recommended distance between the front of the terrace or viewing slope and the playing area is 3 metres where the terrace gradient is 30° or steeper. Where the gradient is shallower than this, it may be advisable to increase this distance so as to enable spectators to obtain a clear view.

10. CRUSH BARRIERS, HANDRAILS AND OTHER PROTECTIVE GUARD RAILS

Many of the hazards arising from crowd pressure on terraces can be eliminated by provision of well constructed, correctly positioned and properly mounted crush barriers which physically control and contain crowd movement. Handrails and other protective guard rails of the correct specification are essential in regulating safe passage of spectators through entry/exit routes.

Dimensions and Design Features

163. In order to locate the top rail against that part of the body most able to tolerate pressure the height of crush barriers should be between 1.02 metres and 1.12 metres above the nosing of the step or standing area immediately behind the barrier, with a preferred height of 1.1 metres (see Figures 7a and 7b).

Figure 7a.
Crush barrier height

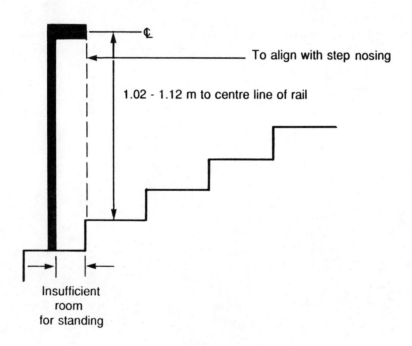

To align with step nosing

1.02 - 1.12 m to centre line of rail

Insufficient room for standing

Height of crush barrier is measured from the step immediately behind the barrier where there is insufficient room for standing on the step on which the barrier is installed.

Figure 7b
Crush barrier height

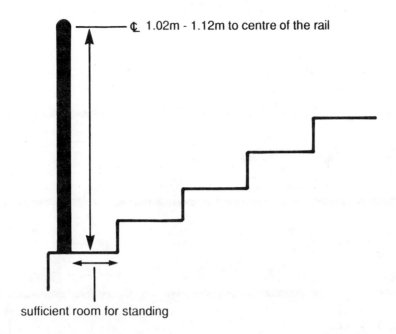

⊄ 1.02m - 1.12m to centre of the rail

sufficient room for standing

164. Crush barriers should be designed so that there are no sharp projections or edges. Although a barrier with a top rail of 50 mm diameter tube has been used at many sports grounds, research has shown that there are advantages in the use of a flat rail of 100 mm vertical depth.

Spacing of Crush Barriers
165. The maximum distance between rows of crush barriers will be dependent on the gradient of the terrace or viewing slope. Paragraphs 168-172 below give details of the spacing and strength of crush barriers.

166. Ideally, crush barriers should be provided along the full width of a terrace, with gaps only at the radial gangways. An example of crush barrier configuration is shown at Figure 8.

Figure 8
Typical layout of radial gangways and pitch perimeter fence gates.

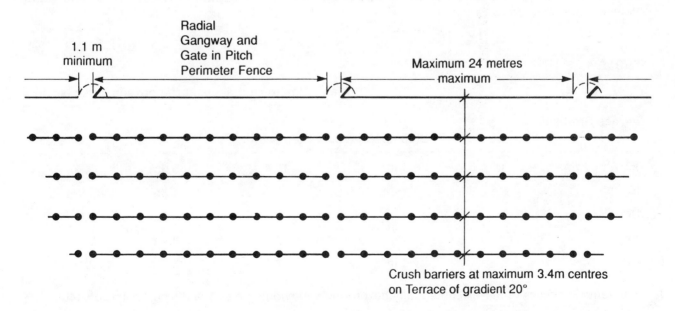

1.1 m minimum

Radial Gangway and Gate in Pitch Perimeter Fence

Maximum 24 metres maximum

Crush barriers at maximum 3.4m centres on Terrace of gradient 20°

35

167. Where it is not practicable for such barriers to be continuous between radial gangways, the alignment of gaps in successive rows of barriers on a terrace should form an angle of less than 60° to the barriers. There should be no more than 2 consecutive gaps in any line. These gaps should be at least 1.1 metres and not more than 1.4 metres in width. (See Figure 9).

Figure 9
Arrangement of gaps between crush barriers

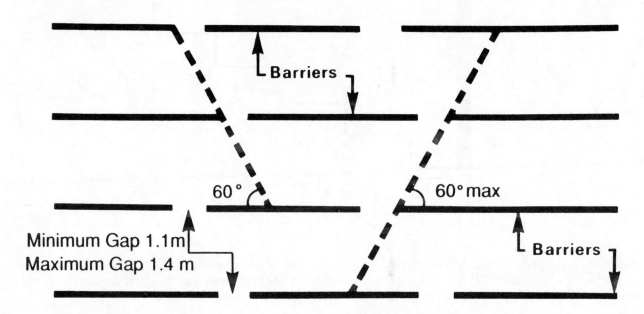

Crush barrier configuration where barriers are not continuous

168. The maximum distance between crush barriers should not exceed the distances shown in Column A of Table 1 for various terrace gradients. At the distances specified, crush barriers should conform to the higher strength requirements for crush barriers set out in Table 2, (ie 5.0 kN/metre width design force or 6.0 kN/metre width test load). Column B of Table 1 sets out the maximum distances between crush barriers which conform to the lower strength requirements of Table 2 (ie 3.4 kN/metre width design force or 4.1 kN/metre width test load.) Interpolation may be made between these figures. (The distinction made in earlier editions of this Guide between 'peak' and other viewing areas is no longer made.)

TABLE 1

				Maximum horizontal distance between crush barriers	
Terrace Gradient		Step riser:	Step width:	A	B
05°	ie	1 in	11.4	5.0m	3.3m
10°		1 in	5.7	4.3m	2.9m
15°		1 in	3.7	3.8m	2.6m
20°		1 in	2.7	3.4m	2.3m
25°		1 in	2.1	3.1m	2.1m

Gradients in excess of this are potentially hazardous and should be avoided (see paragraph 140).

30°		1 in	1.7	2.9m	1.9m

Strength of Crush Barriers, Guardrails and Handrails

169. The structural integrity of crush barriers guardrails and handrails is a major factor in ensuring safety. A 25% representative sample of all, from each part of the ground including stands etc, should be tested annually. Thereafter, the testing of barriers should take place annually so that all barriers are tested at least once every 4 years (see Annex D).

170. All barriers should be visually inspected each year for signs of wear, distortion, corrosion or other signs of weakness. If from such inspections and the records of earlier inspections and tests, there is any doubt as to the integrity of a barrier it should be tested. This test should be in addition to the 25% representative sample.

171. Existing crush barriers and handrails should be capable of resisting the forces indicated in the existing test load columns of Table 2 when applied in a test as described in Annex D. Where existing crush barriers and handrails fail to meet these test conditions, they should be replaced or strengthened in such a way as to do so. Barriers and handrails so strengthened should be retested in accordance with Annex D.

172. New crush barriers or handrails should be designed to resist safely a horizontal force as indicated in the "design force" column in Table 2 applied as a static load acting on the top rail of the barrier or handrail at right angles to the longitudinal axis. The foundations of new barriers or handrails should be designed to resist the overturning moments and sliding forces, induced by the forces described in the "design force" column overleaf, with a factor of safety of 2.

173. New crush barriers designed and constructed in accordance with the provisions of this Chapter will have satisfied the strength requirements and will not therefore require sample testing for 4 years from the date of installation. Such barriers should not form part of the 25% representative sample described in paragraph 169 above. They should however be inspected annually in accordance with paragraph 170 above.

TABLE 2

Table of strengths for crush barriers and handrails

	Design Force for New Barriers	Test Load for Existing Barriers
Crush barriers spaced in accordance with the distances in column A of Table 1	5.0 kN/metre width	6.0 kN/metre width
Crush barriers spaced in accordance with the distances in column B of Table 1	3.4 kN/metre width	4.1 kN/metre width
Handrails at right angles to the direction of flow	3.4 kN/metre width	4.1 kN/metre width
Handrails parallel to the direction of flow	2.2 kN/metre width	2.7 kN/metre width

11. COVERED STANDING AND SEATED ACCOMMODATION

The general safety considerations for covered stands are similar to those for other parts of the ground but with the additional need to safeguard spectators against the greater risk of fire (see Chapter 13).

General

174. Covered stands may consist of seated accommodation only or may contain a mixture of both seated and standing areas. The following advice can be applied to all sports grounds where spectators are so accommodated.

175. The opportunity provided by new design work should be taken to enhance the comfort and amenities for spectators (see paragraphs 23-24, Chapter 1). This is particularly relevant to redevelopment of major football grounds when all-seated stands are provided. New work should conform to the relevant Building Regulations requirements and should be designed on the basis of fire safety engineering principles for the safety of occupants.

176. All spectators should have a clear, unobstructed view of the whole of the playing area. Designs should ensure that sightlines are such that spectators are encouraged to remain seated (where seats are installed) and do not have to strain or stretch to view the playing area. Stands should protect as many spectators as possible from the elements. Exits and exit routes (which will also serve as entrances and entry routes) should be based on the principles set out in Chapters 6 and 7.

Exits

177. There is generally a less hurried departure from the seated accommodation in stands at the end of an event. Moreover, spectators are induced by the layout of the seats to form orderly queues. Even so, attention should be paid to the points below as well as the other structural considerations in respect of stairways, entrances/exits and where appropriate, density levels and crush barriers.

178. There should be sufficient exits to allow for the orderly evacuation of all the spectators. This may entail a reduction in the spectator capacity (see paragraphs 326-330 Chapter 19). Egress/evacuation time used to calculate the exit requirements will depend to a large extent on the fire hazard present (see Chapter 13, paragraphs 241-245) but should be no longer than 8 minutes (see Chapter 7 paragraphs 97-100).

179. Seats and gangways should be so positioned as to provide ready access to exits. No spectator in any part of the seated area should have to travel more than 30 metres from their seat to the nearest exit from the viewing area measured along the line of the seatway and gangway.

Gangways

180. Gangway requirements for standing accommodation are set out in paragraphs 143-151 of Chapter 9. Gangways for seated accommodation should have a slip resistant surface. They should be of sufficient width for the seats served and should be not less than 1.1 metres wide without projections.

181. Any stepped side gangway (ie with viewing accommodation on one side only) should be provided with a hand-rail fixed at a height of not less than 840 mm (measured vertically from the line of the step nosing) and projecting no more than 100 mm into the gangway. The handrail and protective rail should conform to the strength requirement of Table 2, Chapter 10.

182. The going and riser of a stepped gangway in seated accommodation should be uniform. The gradient should not exceed that achieved by the step dimensions for stairways in Chapter 8 paragraph 120 (ie 1 in 1.47 or 34°). Gangways should not contain winders. They need not contain intermediate landings, and the provisions of paragraph 120 (ii) and (iii) on the number of steps and turns which apply to stairways are not appropriate. If, because of site constraints and viewing requirements, the gangways of a stand would result in step dimensions outside those set out in paragraph 120, additional compensatory measures should be provided, as necessary, in order to ensure safe movement on them, for example some form of hand-hold.

Balustrading

183. Those sections of balustrading at the foot of gangways or stairways should be as strong as crush barriers of the stronger type. Other balustrading which will not be subject to pressure from mass crowd movement should conform to normal requirements of Building Regulations and British Standards.

Seating

184. All seats should be securely fixed in position. The use of tip-up seats allows more circulation space, the automatic type being preferable. Upholstered seating should satisfy Ignition Source O of BS 5852 Part 1 and Ignition Source 5 of BS 5852 Part 2.

185. The minimum space allotted to each seated person should be 460 mm wide (500 mm for seats with arms) and 610 mm deep. But for comfort these measurements should be increased to 550 mm and 760 mm respectively.

186. To enable people to move freely between rows of seats there should be at least 305 mm between perpendiculars from the foremost projection of one seat and the back of the seat in front of it, ie the clear seatway or "clearway". The minimum 305 mm is included in the 610 mm and 760 mm depth measurement of the seating area (see Figure 10).

Figure 10.
Minimum dimensions for seating

Minimum seating dimensions
seats with backs

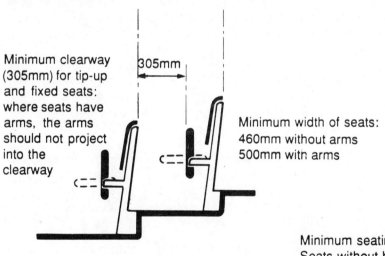

Minimum clearway (305mm) for tip-up and fixed seats: where seats have arms, the arms should not project into the clearway

305mm

Minimum width of seats:
460mm without arms
500mm with arms

Minimum seating dimensions
Seats without backs

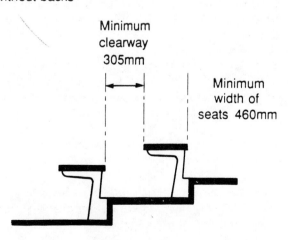

Minimum clearway 305mm

Minimum width of seats 460mm

187. The number of seats in a row should not normally exceed:

a. 14 where there is a gangway at one end only; and

b. 28 where there is a gangway at both ends.

12. TEMPORARY STANDS AND OTHER TEMPORARY STRUCTURES

The principles for securing safety apply to temporary structures to which there are additional considerations.

General

188. The nature of temporary stands and other temporary structures, whether or not covered, used to accommodate spectators at a sports ground is likely to vary considerably as will the materials used in their construction. Some may be erected for a single event only. Even so there is no justification for accepting a lower standard of safety in such structures than elsewhere within the sports ground, and the design and construction of temporary structures should be in accordance with good engineering and building practice, should pay particular regard to public safety and should satisfy all relevant British Standards.

189. The principles of this Guide are applicable to temporary stands and structures and particular attention is drawn to:

Chapter 3   - People with disabilities
Chapter 4   - General Fabric and Structural Matters
Chapter 7   - Egress
Chapter 8   - Stairways and Ramps
Chapter 13 - Fire Safety
Chapter 20 - Recommended Flow Rates

190. All temporary stands should be capable of withstanding any load or force to which they may be subjected and account should be taken of any external factors such as wind forces. Failure of any one support member or connection should not render the structure unstable, cause local, or give rise to progressive, collapse. As far as practicable the area around supporting frames should be secure to prevent unauthorised access, and frames should be so designed that they are firmly locked into position and cannot be tampered with by unauthorised persons.

191. Consultation with the local authority and building authority (if different) should take place at an early stage prior to the erection of any temporary stand. Consultation should also take place with the fire authority about access for fire-fighting purposes.

Siting

192. Choice of location may be limited but factors which need to be considered include: load-bearing capability of the ground, its slope or unevenness, drainage, availability of mains services, access/egress for spectators and for emergency vehicles, overhead power lines, and the proximity of surrounding buildings in relation to the risk of fire. The condition of the site should be regularly checked to ensure its load-bearing capabilities have not deteriorated; settlement of ground may cause instability and so require repacking and relevelling. The site should be prepared and maintained so as to provide an even surface for those parts to which the public have access. In order to be accessible for the disabled the ground surface should be such as to ensure their mobility at all times.

Assembly/Dismantling

193. The assembly and dismantling of stands should be carried out by or under the supervision of persons experienced and trained in the proper performance of such work, in accordance with the manufacturers' instructions whenever available, or in accordance with drawings and specifications prepared by a competent engineer.

194. Work should be carried out only where lighting is sufficient to allow it to be safely and properly performed and checked. No assembly or dismantling work should be carried out to the danger of members of the public in the vicinity.

195. The work should be carried out in a proper manner, using correct parts, and tools of a proper size and design. Care should be taken with the handling of components to avoid damage or distortion.

196. All components should be closely examined during assembly and dismantling for signs of wear, deformation or other damage, and where necessary replaced by sound components of matching material, properties and dimensions. Temporary repairs using makeshift components should be avoided.

197. Care should also be taken to ensure all components are correctly aligned; they should not be bent, distorted or otherwise altered to force a fit.

198. On completion, assembly work should be checked with particular attention given to fastenings and connections.

Tents/marquees and other such structures.

199. These types of structures can present special fire safety problems and guidance is contained in the Home Office/Scottish Office publication "Guide to Fire Precautions in Existing Places of Entertainment and Like Premises" (ISBN O 11 340907 0 £8.50).

200. Tents should be capable of withstanding all forces to which they may be subjected, particularly wind (including uplift so caused) and those caused by the build up of snow or heavy rain. Emergency arrangements should be made for the dismantling, either partial or total, of a tent should abnormal conditions arise that could lead to any collapse or distortion. Where such work in any way affects the stability of the tent or the safety of members of the public, the work should not commence until the immediate area has been cleared of all but essential staff.

201. Supporting poles or structures, guy ropes and stays should be used as necessary, correctly formed and secure anchorages made to ensure that the tent is stable and maintains its correct shape.

202. The stability of the main tent poles and supporting structure should be independent of the sheeting fabric, ie any tearing or defect occurring in the fabric should not result in the collapse of all or any part of the main structure.

203. Particular attention should be paid to the main supporting poles or structures and top braces of large tents where they have to be raised to a considerable height. Damage or distortion to these members could considerably weaken the structure. Where such damage does occur, the members should be replaced or repairs or modifications carried out so as to bring them up to full working strength.

204. Where solid frames or units, eg doors, are linked to a tent structure they should be rigidly formed and adequately braced, and care should be taken that they do not overstress local areas of the tent.

205. Foundations to poles or frames should be properly prepared and subjected to regular checks as should wire bracing or guys, the tension of which should be re-adjusted as necessary.

13. FIRE SAFETY

Safety from fire is achieved by measures which will minimise the risk and restrict the rate of early growth and later spread of fire; provide and protect escape routes; segregate higher fire risk areas; provide fire detection and warning; and assist fire-fighting operations.

General

206. The type of spectator accommodation which is most at risk from fire is the covered stand. Although new buildings will conform to current Building Regulations requiring structural protection from fire, existing structures will vary considerably according to age, condition and materials used in construction. It may therefore be difficult in some cases to improve the fire resistance of an existing structure to any significant extent. But it should be done wherever practicable even though in some cases substantial alterations may be needed to provide reasonable protection from fire (see also paragraph 243).

207. With new stands there is greater opportunity to incorporate comprehensive measures for fire safety and to consider properly the impact of each measure on the others. Design features for new stands should include the following:

    a.   adequate structural resistance to fire;

    b.   fire resisting separation of the viewing accommodation from other parts of the building;

    c.   internal finishes which have low spread of flame characteristics;

    d.   low flammability and fire risk potential in fixtures and fittings, including seating, partitioning and any other fixed or removable contents including cushions;

    e.   contents which are not capable of being easily dismantled or moved to block exit routes;

    f.   no inaccessible places where litter can collect;

    g   a fire warning system, including, where appropriate, automatic fire detection;

    h.   as far as possible no storerooms or other storage areas to form part of the stand building. Where this is unavoidable, such storerooms should be provided with fixed fire extinguishing systems appropriate to the fire risk and should not be accessible from public areas;

    i.   alternative, separated, escape routes which keep people well clear of the smoky gases produced by a fire (which in general means that initial movement of people from the back of the viewing areas should be downwards) and planned in such a way as to avoid the use of the playing area as an escape route;

    j.   the protection of later stages of escape routes so that a continuing fire does not pose any significant threat to them;

    k.   a roof geometry which should restrict smoke and flame travel along the underside of the roof;

    l.   where appropriate, the provision of smoke ventilation within structures.

Minimising fire risk

208. One potential cause of fire arises from the accumulation of waste paper, programmes, food and drink cartons etc dropped by spectators. Such waste can be easily set alight by smokers' materials and the resulting fire may then spread to the structure or the fittings of the building. All parts of the ground should therefore be inspected before and after each event; any accumulation of litter should be cleared away and taken from the ground without delay or kept in a fire-resistant container or room pending removal. Sufficient litter bins should be provided and arrangements made for the frequent emptying of them during an event.

209. Smoking should be discouraged in stands which are constructed of, or contain, combustible or flammable items or materials.

210. A common feature is the existence of voids under the seating and under the flooring itself. These can become a resting place for litter. Seating arrangements should, wherever possible, be such that floor surfaces are accessible for the removal of litter. Voids beneath the floor of the viewing accommodation which are unusable, eg where the viewing area is built on a slope, should, if practicable, be filled with a non-combustible material. Alternatively, they should be either completely sealed off to stop litter accumulating in them, or entirely open in order to allow easy access for inspection and removal of combustible waste.

211. Upholstered seating should satisfy Ignition Source O of BS 5852 Part 1 and Ignition Source 5 of BS 5852 Part 2. Cushioning and other flammable materials, when stored in bulk, pose a risk of a rapid fire growth. They should be stored in a fire-resistant container or room.

212. If it is necessary to store hazardous materials, such as fuels (whether in containers or within fuel tanks and machinery) fertilizers, weed killers and paints, they should be kept in a fire resistant room.

213. Stores used for materials referred to in paragraphs 207, 211 and 212 above should provide access direct from the open air and be well away from public areas and kept locked when not in use. They should be separated from any other part of the building by a construction having a fire resistance of at least 1 hour. When the store has a depth of 6 metres or more, alternative means of escape from it should be provided.

214. High fire risk areas, such as enclosed or underground car parks should be separated from any other part of the building by construction having fire resistance of at least 1 hour.

215. Special care should be taken to ensure that any fuel or power supply used for cooking or heating, in particular LPG cylinders, is safely stored and used, in accordance with the advice of the authority responsible for enforcement of the Health and Safety at Work etc Act 1974. Guidance is given in Health and Safety Executive Guidance Notes CS4, "The Keeping of LPG in Cylinders and Similar Containers" and CS8, "Small Scale Storage and Display of LPG at Retail Premises".

Prevention or retardation of fire growth/spread

216. It is vital to ensure that in the event of a fire the arrangements for escape are preserved by restricting the rate of growth in its early stages. Combustible materials used for fixtures and fittings, or stored, in the building should be kept to a minimum.

217. The viewing accommodation of a stand or other building should be separated from adjacent accommodation or void used for other purposes by a construction which has a fire resistance of at least $^1/_2$ hour. This is so that any fire underneath or in an adjacent area cannot easily break through into the viewing accommodation. The route from the exit from that accommodation (ie the "vomitory exit") should be separated from other internal areas by a construction which has at least one hour fire resistance (see paragraph 238). In such circumstances fire doors, which may disrupt the movement of spectators into the exit route, are unlikely to be necessary on the vomitory exit even if such doors are needed elsewhere in order to protect the exit route.

218. Walls and ceiling linings within viewing accommodation, together with ceiling linings beneath the floor of that accommodation, should have a flame spread classification of not less than Class 1 when tested in accordance with BS 476: Part 7.

219. Fire-fighting equipment and staff trained in "first aid" fire-fighting should be provided in order to tackle any fire without endangering their lives until the fire brigade arrives.

220. Most measures which reduce the rate of fire growth in early stages will also serve to restrict the fire spread in its later stages. For some roof configurations, venting systems may offer a means of reducing the spread of fire (including movement of flames under the roof) and hot smoky gases. The science of fire and smoke venting is, however, complex and advice from the fire authority should be sought on whether this would be advantageous in a particular case.

221. Flammable roof material should not be used. Where it exists it should be replaced by non-combustible materials. Where this is not practicable, it should be underdrawn with non- combustible board.

222. Where the roofs of buildings are close together or connected to each other, smoke or flame should not be allowed to spread from one to another. Unless this risk is eliminated by fire prevention measures, there should be a break in the roof wide enough to prevent that spread.

Fire warning

223. All buildings to which the public or staff have access and which might pose a fire risk should be provided with an electrical fire warning system to alert staff. The system should be designed to accommodate the emergency evacuation procedure of the ground and should be approved by the fire authority. An indication of the warning and its location should be given to a central control point. The system should conform with BS 5839: Part 1 in terms of its components, installation and maintenance.

224. The central control point and, where necessary, other selected positions in the ground should have facilities to call the fire brigade and other emergency services (see Chapter 14). A line of responsibility in contacting the emergency services should be established.

225. The area underneath the spectator accommodation should have a system for detecting fire. Automatic fire detection (AFD) systems in unoccupied areas, conforming to BS 5839: Part 1 in terms of its components, installation and maintenance, should be considered. The alarm should be automatically communicated to the central control point.

226. Fire detection equipment should be tested regularly in accordance with the advice given in the British Standard specification.

227. Where areas of high fire risk such as large storerooms and enclosed or underground car parks are situated under viewing accommodation, consideration should be given to providing an automatic fire extinguishing system, installed in accordance with the relevant part of BS 5306, instead of an AFD system. Activation of the system should be automatically communicated to the central control point.

Emergency lighting

228. Emergency lighting is dealt with in Chapter 15 paragraphs 269-272.

Fire-fighting equipment

229. Advice should be sought from the fire authority on the type, amount and siting of fire-fighting equipment. At some larger grounds it may be necessary to provide a suitable water supply for fire-fighting in the form of hydrants.

230. For "first aid" fire-fighting by members of the staff, consideration should be given to providing hydraulic hose-reels conforming to BS 5306: Part 1. These should be sufficient to provide adequate protection to the whole floor area, and should be installed in a suitable position by entrances, exits and stairways.

231. Where hose-reels are not provided, portable fire extinguishers should be installed in sufficient numbers to give adequate cover. The number and type will depend upon the size, layout, fire separation and risk in each structure. Fire extinguishers should conform to BS 5423 and be sited and maintained according to BS 5306: Part 3.

232. Fire blankets conforming to BS 6575 and suitable fire extinguishers conforming to BS 5423 should be kept in all catering facilities.

233. Fire-fighting equipment should be located so that it cannot be vandalised but is readily accessible to staff in the event of fire.

Emergency procedures and staff training

234. It is essential that plans should be made for dealing with emergencies, including fire (see paragraph 42(vi) Chapter 2).

235. Sufficient staff should be trained in the use of the fire-fighting equipment provided, and/or in the action they should take in the event of fire. The fire authority's advice should be sought on whether the content of the proposed training programme is adequate.

Means of escape

236. "Means of escape" is the structural means whereby a safe route is provided for people to travel from any point in a structure to a place of safety without outside assistance. In existing accommodation, the means of escape in the event of an emergency will usually be the same as the normal exit routes but there may be an additional "route" of forward escape on to the playing area and then out of the ground. All exit routes for use in an emergency should be clearly signposted (see paragraph 101, Chapter 7) and should be capable of being safely and effectively used at all times when the ground is occupied.

237. The emergency exit routes should be sited so that people using them will be least affected by the fire or its products, for example smoke, toxic gases, and heat. Initial travel should if possible be downwards. This is because in the event of fire, its dangerous products will travel upwards and accumulate densely at the highest points. Further stages of the exit routes should be so arranged as to take people progressively further away from the fire, along a route where they cannot be significantly affected by the fire or its products. There should be more than one emergency exit route from a viewing area and the exit system should be such that any blockage in one exit does not prevent access to an alternative.

Fire protection for stairways and passages

238. Where a stairway, passage or any other part of an emergency exit route passes up, down or through a stand or other building used by spectators, unless it is in the open air, it should be in a fire resistant enclosure separated from the remainder of the stand by a structure having fire resistance of not less than one hour. Such exit routes should discharge to a place of safety in the open air (see also paragraph 132).

239. The surface finish of walls and ceilings of all emergency exit routes above should be of a standard corresponding to Class O (as defined in the guidance issued in connection with the Building Regulations for England and Wales and the Building Standards (Scotland) Regulations).

240. Any door forming part of the enclosure to an exit route should be self closing and have a fire resistance of not less than half an hour (see also paragraph 217 above).

Emergency evacuation time

241. The evacuation time is an arbitrary time which, together with the maximum flow-rate figure, is used to determine the capacity of the exit route(s) providing the means of escape from the viewing accommodation in an emergency (see paragraph 236). This exit capacity is a factor in calculating the number of spectators who can be accommodated (see Chapter 19 paragraphs 313 and 326).

242. The emergency evacuation time will depend largely on the level of fire risk present in the accommodation. Spectator accommodation which has, for any reason, the potential for rapid fire spread should have an exit capacity based on an evacuation time of not more than $2^1/2$ minutes. An increase in this time will be acceptable where the possibility of rapid fire spread is reduced by the provision of fire safety measures (either active or passive systems) and the emergency exit routes are not vulnerable to a fire occurring within the building. For example, an open concrete terrace or a stand which incorporates the fire safety design features described in paragraph 207 above, where spectators are not totally enclosed and can move into protected exit routes, or exit routes in the open air, would normally have an exit capacity based on an 8 minute calculation (see Chapter 6 paragraph 97).

243. The conditions within a particular ground may call for interpolation between the times referred to in paragraph 242 above. The aim should always be to introduce measures which will minimise the outbreak and spread of fire rather than rely on an exit capacity based on a $2^1/_2$ minute calculation as a solution (see also paragraph 206). In all cases, the advice of the fire authority should be sought.

244. Advice on the calculation of exits required for internal areas of a stand or other building occupied by spectators, for example, a restaurant or bar, is contained in the Guide to Fire Precautions in Existing Places of Entertainment and Like Premises.

245. Where the playing area or perimeter track is accessible to spectators and is considered as a part of the exit route, exits onto it from the viewing accommodation can be taken into account when calculating the capacity of that exit system. Where there is a pitch perimeter fence, wall or moat, it should have access points in accordance with Chapter 18, paragraph 300 which can serve as emergency exits for that purpose.

246. Where the playing surface of a pitch is made of synthetic materials, advice from the fire authority should be sought to establish if it can be properly considered an emergency exit route in the event of a fire. This is because it is possible that some forms of artificial turf might in themselves constitute a hazard in the event of fire because of flamespread and fumes etc caused by decomposition of the material as a result of heat radiation and ignition.

247. If the playing area is wholly surrounded by covered accommodation with no breaks in the roofing (see paragraph 222) it may not be suitable for evacuation in the event of fire and the advice of the fire authority should be sought.

Access for emergency vehicles
248. Adequate roads for emergency vehicles should be provided so that speedy and direct access can be obtained to all buildings within the ground. Wherever possible these access routes should be separate from those used by spectators entering and leaving the ground or, alternatively, provide for the parking of emergency vehicles so that routes used by crowds are not seriously obstructed. The police and the fire authority should be consulted about the suitability of access roads and access to the ground.

249. Where practicable and necessary, roads within $^1/_4$ of a mile of the ground should be kept entirely free of parked vehicles so as not to delay or obstruct emergency vehicles.

14. COMMUNICATIONS

There should be a communications system capable of clearly relaying essential messages to both staff and spectators in all parts of the ground, inside and outside, in both normal and emergency conditions.

General

250. Precise requirements for communications will depend on the sort of ground and the numbers of people that attend there. Professional advice and expertise should be sought and, in general, the communications system should be determined after consultation with the local authority (where a safety certificate is in force), police, fire and ambulance services. The system should conform to relevant British Standards or Code of Practice. It should be available for use, capable of coping with all emergencies and should have an override facility. It should provide the central control and, where necessary, selected positions in the ground, the facility to call the emergency services. It is ground management who should provide and operate the necessary equipment for this purpose as well as provide competent staff, suitably trained in its use.

Central Control

251. There should be a central control room commanding a good view of the whole ground from which the communications system should operate. It should contain the facility to communicate quickly with staff, the public and the emergency services. Subject to paragraphs 259-260 below the safety officer and his staff should be responsible for the operation of the communications system.

252. There should be inter-communication between the central control, all turnstiles or banks of turnstiles and all entry and exit gates used by the public (see also Chapter 6). Metering systems to record all admissions should be installed at turnstiles and, to ensure that ground capacities are not exceeded, arrangements should be made for central control and police control room where provided to be informed immediately a predetermined number of spectators has been admitted through each turnstile, or bank of turnstiles serving each section of the ground.

Public Address/System Warning

253. The public address system should be able to communicate with individual areas outside and inside the ground, with groups of areas or with the whole ground.

254. Emergency use of the system as part of the fire warning system means that it will also need to comply with BS 5389 Part 1 (Code of practice for system design, installation and servicing of Fire Detection and Alarm Systems in Buildings).

255. Important announcements relating to crowd safety should be preceded by a loud signal to catch the attention of the crowd despite a high level of noise in the ground. This signal, followed by the voice-over transmission should be different to, and distinct from, any other signals which may be in general use on the system. This arrangement should be prominently displayed in every programme sold for every event.

256. The public address equipment should be installed so that broadcast messages can be heard under reasonable conditions (including emergencies) by all persons of normal hearing in any part of the ground to which the public has access. Installation should conform to the relevant guidance contained in BS 6259 (Code of Practice for Planning and Installation of Sound Systems). The power supply to the system should be such as to enable it to continue to operate in an emergency, such as fire or a failure of the mains supply, for up to 3 hours.

257. In the event of an emergency it is essential that clear, accurate information is given to spectators at the earliest possible time. Messages should be positive leaving those to whom they are addressed in no doubt as to what is required of them. They should be pre-arranged, worded with the agreement of the police, fire authority and, where a safety certificate is in force, the local authority.

Back-up Provision

258. Loud hailers should be available for the use of stewards and police in all parts of the ground for directing or instructing spectators.

259. Any police radio facilities available for the maintenance of law and order should augment and not be regarded as a substitute for the ground communications system.

Police Control Room

260. Where there is sufficient special police presence inside the ground to warrant a police control room, such a room should be provided for use by the officer in charge. This control may be in addition to that used by the ground safety officer in which case an adjoining or a joint control room should be considered. There must be a clear, unequivocal understanding by both police and management as to the tasks, duties and responsibilities which will be undertaken by the police and those which will be undertaken by the ground management (see also Chapter 17, paragraph 286). There must be established lines of communication between them.

261. International grounds, grounds of clubs in the English Football League and clubs in the Premier Division of the Scottish Football League should provide a police control room which is:-

(a) well placed so as to command a good view of the whole pitch and the spectators surrounding it;

(b) of sufficient size for the officer in charge, his deputy, management representative and enough officers to operate radios, telephones and any other equipment. There should be space for others who may need to visit the room, for example, other senior officers, management, representatives of the emergency services and local authority;

(c) properly equipped with suitable CCTV, radio, telephone facilities.

262. Where necessary the control room should be sound-proofed against excessive noise. The room and equipment should be to the satisfaction of the chief officer with responsibility for the ground.

263. To complement police radio communications there should be a separate system of land-lines with telephone links between control room and key points, for example, turnstiles, stewards' control point, secretary's office, referee's room, lighting control, medical practitioner, casualty clearance points and first aid room.

Close Circuit Television

264. Consideration should be given to the installation of CCTV in order to monitor turnstiles (inside and outside the ground) ingress/egress routes, concourse areas, terraces and any other area where there is likely to be a crowd build-up. CCTV should normally be installed for this purpose at grounds used for major events and in particular at grounds referred to in paragraph 261 above. Before decisions are reached, analysis of each ground is necessary. Each part of the spectator accommodation should be assessed for the nature and degree of risk in order to determine whether CCTV will be of use, if so, the individual needs and whether alternative measures can be taken which achieve equal or better results.

265. Guidance on CCTV, based on research carried out by Home Office, Police Scientific Development Branch, can be obtained from the Home Office, Queen Anne's Gate, London SW1H 9AT.

15. AUXILIARY POWER

Auxiliary power should be available and be sufficient to enable emergency lighting, the Public Address system CCTV and other electrically powered installations to function for at least 3 hours after the failure of the normal supply.

General

266. In the event of a power failure consideration should be given to cancellation of the event. If the auxiliary power supply is capable of supplying the entire load for the ground for at least 3 hours it may be possible to continue a fixture or event provided it is scheduled to finish and the ground cleared within this period and no other emergency situation exists. To supply such a load a generator rather than a central battery system is likely to be required. An additional back up emergency power supply will be necessary if an event is to continue. Ground management should take into account the needs for the ground in deciding the type of power provision and make contingency plans for the failure of the power supply (see Chapter 2).

267. Auxiliary power equipment should be located in a secure room to which the public does not have access. The room should be of fire-resisting construction of a standard of not less than 1 hour.

268. All equipment should be installed, maintained and tested in accordance with the manufacturers instructions and relevant British Standards.

Emergency lighting

269. Emergency lighting, for use in the event of a failure of the general lighting, should be provided in all parts of the premises accessible to the public and along all exit routes, with exit signs clearly illuminated. Installation should be in accordance with BS 5266: Part 1. The system should be completely separate from the normal lighting system, although a one-circuit system incorporating staggered sub-circuits would be an acceptable alternative. Unless, exceptionally, two entirely independent supplies can be obtained from outside sources, the emergency circuit should be connected to a source of power located on the premises, for example storage batteries or a diesel generator, with a delay of not more than 5 seconds.

270. The system should be capable of maintaining the necessary level (see IES Lighting Code) of illumination for a period of 3 hours from the time of failure of the normal supply.

271. The emergency lighting should operate automatically on the failure of the normal lighting.

272. Emergency lighting systems should be tested regularly in accordance with BS 5266: Part 1.

Public Address System

273. Where the public address system is part of the fire warning system it should conform to BS 5839 Part 1 (see Chapter 13 paragraph 223 and Chapter 14 paragraph 254). Auxiliary power will in such circumstances therefore be needed to ensure the continued use of the system in the event of fire or other emergency.

16. STEWARDING

Effective stewarding should prevent overcrowding in sections of the ground, reduce the likelihood and incidence of disorder, help disperse spectators in such a way as to reduce crowd pressure and provide the means to investigate, report and take early action in an emergency.

General
274. It should be emphasised to stewards that they are deployed to assist in the safe operation of the ground, not to view the activity taking place.

275. Staffing levels and stewarding requirements will vary depending upon the size and configuration of the ground, the nature of the event and crowd levels, but there are six basic duties which stewards are called upon to carry out. These are:

a) to control or direct spectators who are entering or leaving the ground, to help achieve an even flow of people to the viewing areas;

b) to recognise crowd densities, signs of crowd distress and crowd dynamics so as to help ensure safe dispersal of spectators on the terraces or viewing slopes;

c) to patrol the ground to deal with any emergencies eg. raising alarms or tackling the early stages of fires;

d) to staff entrances, exits to and from the viewing accommodation and other strategic points, especially exit doors and exit gates from the ground which are not continuously open whilst the ground is in use;

e) to assist police as appropriate or as requested with crowd control; and

f) to undertake specific duties in an emergency.

276. A more detailed check list of the kind of duties which stewards are liable to undertake is at Annex E. It should be borne in mind that this is not necessarily an exhaustive list of duties.

277. Management should appoint a chief steward responsible for co-ordinating responsibilities of all stewards. The chief steward should attend police pre-match briefing. Control of stewards should be from a central point with an efficient means to communicate with them (see also Chapter 14).

Age and Fitness
278. Stewards should be fit, active, not less than age 18 and ideally not more than 55 years old. They should be fully capable of carrying out the duties allocated to them. Every steward should be fully appraised in writing of his duties and responsibilities and should carry on him a general check list of them.

Training
279. Where a ground, such as one used by an association football league club, has special police presence, duties and responsibilities of stewards should be agreed with the police and form part of any written understanding or statement of intent agreed with the police. Stewards should attend pre-match briefing and should be made aware as necessary of the arrangements and any contingency plans to deal with the arrival of away supporters.

280. Effective training and supervision should be provided by management so that all stewards, whether regular or casual, know not only what their duties are but how to carry them out and why. This is especially important in emergencies when it is essential that stewards and their supervisors are fully aware of, and practiced in, the part they are to play in the plans drawn up with the emergency services. Exercises should be carried out before the start of, and mid-way through, the season so as to ensure that emergency procedures operate smoothly. A record should be kept of the duration of the exercise, details of the instruction given and by whom. At least 14 days' notice of the intention to hold such exercises should be given to the local authority (if a safety certificate is in force), the police, fire and ambulance services.

Identification

281. All stewards should be readily identifiable eg. by the wearing of distinctive clothing such as luminous tabards which are numbered and distinctive from those worn by police, fire and ambulance services. Armbands are not acceptable.

Visiting Stewards

282. At association football grounds any supplementary stewards from visiting clubs who will be operational during an event must arrive before the ground is open to the public and in time to be fully briefed as to the construction and configuration of the ground, the safety arrangements and their specific duties.

17. CROWD BEHAVIOUR

Where there is a disorderly element among the crowd intent on violence, additional safety measures are needed to contain and minimise the potential disruption, to isolate quickly, identify and remove the offenders and to prevent their re-entry on future occasions.

General

283. Although the problem of crowd disorder at sporting events is one which affects primarily professional association football, other sports are not immune from it. Therefore, whilst the following advice is directed mainly at those grounds where professional association football is played, especially grounds used by English Football League clubs, the general principles should also be borne in mind by managements at other grounds where major spectator sports are played.

284. The 'European Convention on Spectator Violence and Misbehaviour at Sporting Events and in particular at Football Matches' (HMSO, Cmmd 9649), which came into force on 1 November 1985, sets out in general terms measures to be taken to prevent and control violence by spectators. The Standing Committee on the Convention in April 1989 adopted a comprehensive report on measures to counter hooliganism and guidelines on ticket sales. In addition all clubs in the Football League are required by League regulations to have in place local plans for crowd control and safety, drawn up in consultation with local authorities, local police and other relevant organisations.

285. For matches in European competitions, UEFA has issued binding instructions in their document 'Order and Security in the Stadia' (Third Edition, 1985). The following paragraphs cover some of the main areas that require the attention of ground management. The advice they contain is not comprehensive and is intended to supplement rather than replace existing instructions, codes of practice etc.

Policing

286. Although the measures described elsewhere in the Guide will help achieve reasonable safety at a sports ground, for management to discharge its responsibility properly, a special police presence inside the ground may be necessary. The number and disposition of the police must be determined by the Chief Police Officer in whose area the ground is located. Where there is such a presence there should be a clear, written understanding or 'statement of intent' agreed between the police and the ground management setting out the functions and responsibilities of each as to crowd safety. A copy of the statement should be available to the local authority. Dealing with disorder (as distinct from normal ground operations and crowd management on the premises) as in any other circumstances will fall to the police.

287. Ground managements should give all possible assistance to the police and provide police control facilities within the ground (see also Chapter 14, paragraph 260).

288. Proper advance planning with the police is essential to counter potential crowd disorder. There must be an effective liaison between club and police for this purpose to include not just the arrangements inside the ground but also the escort of visiting supporters, their likely numbers, their separate entry to the ground and their departure at the end of the match. There should be debriefing meetings as necessary to evaluate existing arrangements and provide the flexibility necessary to deal with different circumstances.

Crowd movement

289. If crowd movement is to be controlled by the sub-division of terraces or viewing slopes by structural means, such as railings or fences, in order to help the police contain any disorder, the greatest care must be taken to ensure that these sub-divisions cannot be filled beyond their specified safe limit. Dividing structures should comply with the strength requirements set out in Chapter 10. Each sub-division should be assessed for its safe limit, the limit specified, recorded and arrangements made to ensure it is not exceeded. Each sub-division should be self-contained, serviced by its own entrances/exits, refreshment facilities and toilets - in keeping with the principles of Chapter 6 and paragraphs 152-153 of Chapter 9. If the sub-divisions are not self-contained and arrangements cannot be made to keep a reliable count of spectators admitted to them, they must not be used. Alternatively, the sub-dividing fences should be removed and the whole area controlled as a complete section.

290. Proposals which entail changes in the configuration of the viewing accommodation or entry/egress to and from it, for example for the purposes of segregation, should be acted upon by ground management only after full account has been taken of their effect on the safe movement, evacuation arrangements and the holding capacity. Where a safety certificate is in force the local authority should be consulted about such proposals.

Segregation

291. Home and visiting supporters at professional association football matches may have to be segregated but segregation is not advocated for other sports where crowd disorder is not a problem.

292. Where possible a neutral or sterile zone should be provided within a ground so that home and visiting supporters are not physically close to each other. The arrangements for admitting spectators into the ground, whether by tickets purchased in advance or through payment at the turnstiles, should be drawn up in consultation with the police, and must be carefully controlled to ensure as far as possible that segregation is effective and known troublemakers are excluded.

293. Segregation arrangements may also have to include measures which deter spectators from invading the pitch or playing area. At the same time the arrangements will need to provide for the police to have effective access to the terraces in the event of an outbreak of violence. Moreover, where the playing area is accessible for evacuation in an emergency, any structural means used to deter unauthorised encroachment onto the pitch, must allow for such access (see also Chapter 18).

Detention and removal of trouble makers

294. At soccer grounds, where there has been a record of frequent crowd trouble, secure detention rooms should be provided if requested by the police.

295. There should be adequate vehicular access for the unobtrusive removal of detainees (see also Chapter 13, paragraphs 248-249 on access for emergency vehicles).

Refreshments

296. Hard containers such as glasses, bottles or cans can make dangerous missiles and should not be used for the sale of refreshments. All refreshments should be served in soft containers. Adequate receptacles should be available for rubbish disposal and collection (paragraph 208).

297. Alcohol should not be on sale for consumption on the terraces or in the seated accommodation.

298. Ground managements should also note that the Sporting Events (Control of Alcohol etc) Act 1985 applies to any ground in England and Wales used for an international association football match or a match involving a football league club. In Scotland the Criminal Justice (Scotland) Act 1980 applies to grounds used by clubs in the Scottish Football League, Highland League and to the international stadia used for association football and Rugby Union.

18. PITCH PERIMETER FENCE/WALL

A pitch perimeter fence/wall may not only delineate the playing area from the spectator accommodation but may have to serve as a crush barrier, and in some situations will serve as a means to discourage or prevent access to the playing area except in an emergency.

General

299. The type, strength and height of a pitch perimeter fence or wall will vary according to its location and required function. At one extreme, at a certain type of ground or small stadium used by very few spectators, there may be no need for a perimeter fence or wall at all; or if such a wall or fence exists it may need to consist of little more than a rail to mark the playing area. At the other extreme, some major soccer stadia may have a fence which prevents access to the pitch in normal circumstances (see also Chapter 17, paragraph 293) but allows for access in emergency as part of the measures taken to prevent or contain any outbreak of crowd disorder. Such a fence may be limited to one part of the ground, for example, the "away supporters end" or it might encompass other sections.

Access to the playing area

300. Any pitch fence or wall, whatever its height, which delineates the spectator area from the playing area restricts or impedes access to the pitch. The extent of the restriction depends upon the nature of the fence or wall. All pitch fences and walls must therefore contain gates or openings (if no gates are fitted) which allow access to the playing area or any perimeter track. Openings should be no less than 1.1 metres wide. They should align with radial gangways (where provided) and should be not less than the width of those gangways. Openings or gates should be properly stewarded, should be clearly marked and painted a different colour from the rest of the fence or wall. Gates, where fitted, should open away from the spectators and should be kept unlocked.

Strength

301. If spectators can lean on the perimeter fence or wall it should be deemed a crush barrier and fulfil the conditions of height and strength specified in Chapter 9 except that if the fence is of solid construction its height may be more than 1.12 metres. This is because the pressures acting on a person forced against such a fence are distributed over a large area of the body, unlike the situation with a normal crush barrier, where the pressures are localized.

Pitch Barrier Fences

302. The term "pitch barrier fence" in the following paragraphs means any pitch fence or wall which exceeds the maximum recommended height of a crush barrier (1.12 metres) measured from the spectator accommodation side of the fence or wall.

303. Pitch barrier fences are not normally considered to be necessary except at sports grounds used by association football clubs, especially clubs, in the English football league. They are usually associated with standing areas rather than seated areas and (with some exceptions) are not generally considered necessary when seated accommodation extends to the level of the playing area. Similarly family or club enclosures are unlikely to require such a fence.

304. Whether a pitch barrier fence is installed will depend on individual circumstances, such as a history of hostile pitch invasions or other disorder from a certain part of the ground, the extent to which stewarding and policing is felt to be able to deal with any attempted encroachment of the pitch and availability of alternative solutions.

305. Where a pitch barrier fence is installed it should not impair visibility of the playing area. If sightlines from a terrace are obscured congestion may be caused, for example because spectators are unwilling to move forward, or seated spectators induced to stand up. If such problems are not resolved satisfactorily, consequential reductions in capacity should result, see Chapter 19.

306. The maximum height of a pitch barrier fence should be 2.2 metres. There should be no overhanging sections and no spikes, barbed wire or other devices installed or attached to it.

307. All pitch barrier fences must contain gates or openings as described in paragraph 300 above. If a terrace is sub-divided by structural means (see Chapter 9 paragraph 153, and Chapter 17 paragraph 289) each sub-division must have its own gate or gates leading onto the pitch. There must be sufficient pitch gates in each such sub-division capable of evacuating all the spectators in that sub-division onto the playing area within the emergency evacuation time set for that section of the viewing accommodation (see Chapter 13 paragraphs 241-247 and also Chapter 19 Example G).

308. Whenever practicable to do so terraces should not descend to a pitch barrier fence (see Figure 11). A walkway between the fence and the terrace should if possible be created and reserved solely for use by police, club and first-aid personnel. In order to achieve this it may be necessary to take out of use or remove completely one or two rows of terracing. The walkway would need to be protected by continuous crush barriers in order to discourage access except in an emergency via authorised points (ie radial gangways).

Figure 11.
Cross section showing walkway between terraces and pitch fence/wall.

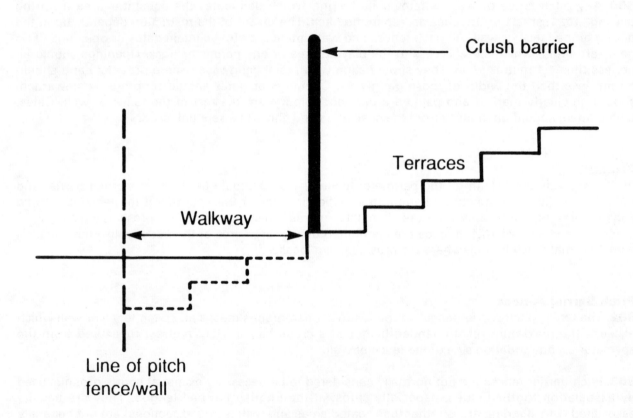

309. As an additional precaution, consideration should be given, in consultation with the local authority if a safety certificate is in force, to the provision of suitable equipment wherever pitch barrier fencing is installed so that, if necessary, sufficient fencing can be removed in order to release any trapped spectators. Trained operators provided by the club should be available in order to use the equipment. The nominated senior police officer will decide when such equipment is to be used.

19. ASSESSMENT OF SAFE GROUND CAPACITY

To assess the number of spectators which can be safely accommodated account should be taken of the features of the individual ground, its configuration, general condition, intended use and any deviations from the Guide's provisions.

General

310. The previous sections of the Guide give guidelines and safety considerations for individual features of a ground. This section describes a method of calculating the number of spectators that can be safely accommodated when taking into account interactions between these individual features and where there are deviations from the guidelines. It may be necessary to calculate various capacities if the ground is used for more than one activity.

311. The calculations should be attached to a plan of the ground and should be available with such details as exits, stands, terraces, stairways, passages, kiosks, seats and barriers. A scale of 1:200 should be used for this purpose. The plan should be cross referenced and attached to the calculations.

312. The method assesses:

    a. the holding capacity of a terrace or viewing slope (that of a seated area generally being determined either by the number of seats when it conforms to guidelines, or an acceptable reduced occupancy when the guidelines can not be met); and

    b. the capacity of a given exit/entry route from a terrace or stand.

313. The number of people that can be safely accommodated on a terrace or in a stand (or other covered accommodation) is either its holding capacity, or the capacity of the exit/entry system to be used in normal circumstances or the emergency exit system, whichever is the least.

Holding capacity of terraces and viewing slopes

314. An even distribution of spectators on a terrace or viewing slope is likely to be difficult to achieve notwithstanding the measures described in this guide because spectators may prefer to gather in a certain part or parts of the viewing area. This pattern of crowd dispersal and any other relevant factors should be taken into consideration when assessing the safe capacity for a particular area.

315. In all cases the calculation of the capacity of the standing area should take into account only those parts of the viewing accommodation from which the whole of the playing area can be seen excluding gangways, stairways and landings (ie the "available viewing area" for calculation purposes). Where a viewing slope has an insufficient gradient to provide a clear view, the depth of the crowd taken for calculation purposes should be a maximum of two metres. If the positioning and/or width of the gangways do not meet the criteria of paragraphs 143-151 of Chapter 9 a commensurate reduction should be made to the available viewing area.

316. *Where crush barriers conform* to the specifications in Chapter 10 and the viewing area is in good condition (see Chapter 9) the maximum allowable overall packing density is 47 persons per 10 square metres over the available viewing area. Where the conditions of the viewing area materially deviate from Chapter 9 a reduction must be made in the packing density. There is no lower limit to this reduction, and if a viewing area is in such poor condition that it is unfit for use, the figure is 0. Interpolation between these figures will be necessary where the conditions fall between the two extremes.

317. The capacity of the standing area is calculated by multiplying the area available for standing by the appropriate packing density. The following formula may be used:

$$\text{Capacity (Number of persons)} = \frac{A \times D}{10}$$

where 'A' is the area available for standing in square metres and 'D' is the density, between 0 and 47.

Example A

318. Barriers and pitch perimeter wall conform to the Guide's recommendations on construction, height, strength and spacing.
Net available viewing area: 76 metres x 16 metres = 1216 square metres (excluding designated gangways).

Condition and drainage of terraces good.

Dimensions: steps 360 mm width (Guide recommends 280 mm - 375 mm, see Chapter 9, paragraph 139)
risers 70 mm* (Guide recommends 75 mm - 180 mm, see Chapter 9, paragraph 140)

* Correction not possible without major reconstruction so accepted in view of only minor deviation of 5 mm and good condition of the terrace:- ie fully acceptable for 47 persons per 10 square metres.

Capacity: $1216 \times \dfrac{47}{10} = 5715$

Example B (where there is material deviation from the Guide)

319. Gross area of the viewing accommodation for standing: 76 x 16 = 1216 square metres.

Condition of terrace: acceptable but

    a)   some unevenness caused by repair work

    b)   some cracking and rough surface in places

    c)   no gangways.

Required gangway provision (see Figure 12) determined as:-

1 lateral gangway at rear leading to exit stairways: ie 1 at 1.1 metres by 76 =   83.6 square metres

4 radial gangways: ie 4 at 1.1 by 14.9 = 65.6 square metres_____

Total 149.2

Available viewing area = 1216 - 149.2 = 1066.8 square metres

Packing density determined at 35 per 10 square metres to allow for underfoot conditions.

Capacity $1066.8 \times \dfrac{35}{10} = 3734$

Note: Figure of 3734 is below 3960 quoted in example E. Therefore, any upgrading of terracing to accommodate more than 3960 spectators would also require installation of additional turnstiles and improvements (if any) to entry routes.

Figure 12.
Available viewing area and gangway position of standing accommodation

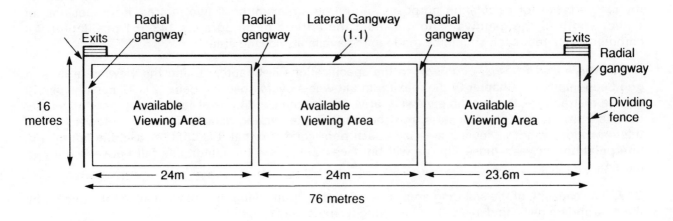

PITCH

Note: All spectators are within 12 metres of a gangway or exit.

320. *If the crush barriers meet the height and strength* criteria set down in Chapter 10 *but do not conform* to the distances laid down in Table 1, or if the gaps between them are greater than those described in paragraphs 168 and Figure 11 of Chapter 10, the capacity of the viewing area is calculated from the provision of crush barriers. The total length of crush barriers (including the pitch wall or fence if it serves as, and meets the requirements of, a crush barrier) should be measured. This figure is then multiplied by either the recommended distance between the barriers (see Table 1) or the actual distance whichever is the lesser. This establishes the notional available viewing area (see Figure 13). This area is then multiplied by the density factor determined for that area.

Figure 13.
Notional available viewing area when crush barriers do not conform.

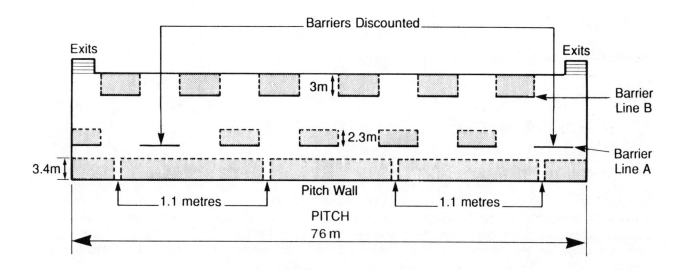

Example C (Spacing and distance of crush barriers do not conform to Chapter 10)

321. Gross area of the viewing accommodation for standing 76 x 16 = 1216 square metres. Terrace steps conform to dimensions of Chapter 8: drainage and condition good.

Terrace gradient 20° (1 in 2.7)

Crush barrier configuration as in Figure 13.

Working load of pitch wall established by test meets the *higher* strength of Table 2 Chapter 10.

Crush barriers consist of 12 at 6 metres in length plus 1 at 3 metres in length.

Test/inspection of two barriers (see Figure 13) reveal sufficient doubts as to their integrity and are discounted for calculation purposes.

Remaining barriers in Line A (see Figure 13) have a safe working load (established by test) of the lower strength of Table 2.

Barriers in Line B have a safe working load (established by test) of the higher strength of Table 2.

Calculation of (notional) available viewing area:

    (a) Pitch wall: 76 metres less 4 exits at 1.1 = 71.6 metres. Recommended crush barrier distance (for higher strength) on a gradient of 20° = 3.4 metres (actual distance from pitch wall to crush barriers 5 metres). Notional available viewing area is therefore 71.6 x 3.4 = 243.4 square metres.

(b) Crush barriers: Line A = 4 at 6 metres plus 1 at 3 metres = 27 metres. Recommended distance between barriers (for lower strength) 2.3 metres (actual distance 8 metres). Notional available viewing area is therefore 27 x 2.3 = 62.1 square metres.

Crush barriers: Line B = 6 at 6 metres = 36 metres. Recommended distance between barriers (for higher strength) 3.4 metres. Actual distance behind barriers is 3 metres. Notional available viewing area is therefore 36 x 3 = 108 square metres.

Total notional available viewing area:-

$$\begin{array}{r} 243.4 \\ 62.1 \\ \underline{108.0} \\ 413.5 \end{array}$$

Packing density 47 per 10 square metres.

Capacity = 413.5 x $\dfrac{47}{10}$ = 1943

Note:- average packing density for standing area as a whole would therefore equate to

$\dfrac{1943}{1216}$ x 10 = 16 per 10 square metres.

322. Terraces or viewing slopes at older grounds not used for major sporting fixtures and which are attended by very few spectators may not have crush barriers at all; or if they do their installation may be random and not meet the specifications of Chapter 10. The safe capacity in such circumstances has to be assessed on the conditions prevailing at the ground. All relevant factors have to be considered eg underfoot condition, the dispersal of the crowd at fixtures. The overall capacity of the terrace will be limited and the average packing density will be low. One method of calculation is taken from the pitch wall/fence (if any) discounting the rest of the terrace.

Example D

323. Gross area of the viewing accommodation for standing area 76 x 16 = 1216 square metres.

No pitch wall: spectator accommodation bounded by a rail around the pitch and does not conform to the specification of Chapter 18, paragraph 301.

Allow spectators a (notional) standing area of 76 metres by, say, four terrace steps at 36.0 mm per step: ie, 76 x 1.44 = 109.44 square metres.

Available standing area (notional) = 109.44 square metres.

Underfoot conditions good.

Capacity = 109.44 x $\dfrac{47}{10}$ = 514

Turnstile Capacity
324. The number of turnstiles may, however, determine how many spectators can be accommodated in the viewing accommodation if they cannot pass through them in at least 1 hour.

Example E

325. Net available viewing area 76 metres x 16 metres = 1216 square metres.

Crush barriers and terrace conform to standards described in Example A above.

Number of turnstiles serving the area = 6
Measured turnstile rate exceeds 660 per hour.
Maximum acceptable rate for calculation purposes - 660

Capacity = 660 x 6 = 3960

Exit Capacity

326. General considerations to be taken into account when assessing the adequacy of exit systems are set out in Chapter 7. The capacity of an exit system can be calculated by assessing for each element in the system (ie each gangway, doorway, stairway, exit etc) the number of persons who can pass the limiting point in that element in 8 minutes (ie egress time, see Chapter 7, paragraph 97). The capacity of the emergency exit system is the number of people who can pass through the designated emergency exit route in the appropriate emergency evacuation time (see Chapter 13 paragraphs 241-247). The calculation is made as follows:-

$$\frac{\text{Width of element}}{\text{Unit width (.550)}} \times \begin{array}{c}\text{appropriate} \\ \text{flow rate} \\ \text{(See Chapter 20)}\end{array} \times \begin{array}{c}\text{appropriate} \\ \text{time}\end{array}$$

327. Where an element in the exit system is less than 1 metre wide that element should be omitted from the calculation.

Example F

328. Net available viewing area 76 x 16 = 1216 square metres excluding designated gangways.

Maximum potential capacity =

$1216 \times \dfrac{47}{10} = 5715$ (see example A).

Exit capacity consists of 2 stairways in each corner of the terrace leading to a concourse at the rear, converging on 1 exit gate in the centre. (See Figure 14.1.)

Analysis of exit capacity allowing a minimum of 8 minutes for spectators to pass through a fixed point, using flow rates given in Chapter 20.

Stairways = 3.327 metres. These are divided into two channels of 1.1 metres and one channel of 1.127 metres.

Each stairway capacity is therefore:-

$\dfrac{3.327}{.550} \times 40 \times 8 = 1935.7$ (1936)

The capacity of the passage or concourse at the rear of the terrace is measured at its narrowest points (see Figure 14.1). In sector A the distance measured is 3.05 metres. Exit capacity at this point is calculated as:-

$\dfrac{3.05}{.550} \times 60 \times 8 = 2661.8$ (2662)

In sector B the narrowest point is measured as 4 metres. Exit capacity at this point is calculated as:-

$\dfrac{4.0}{.550} \times 60 \times 8 = 3490.9$ (3491)

The exit gate is measured as 4.88 metres.

The exit capacity of the gate is calculated as:-

$\dfrac{4.88}{.550} \times 60 \times 8 = 4258.9$ (4259)

From the above calculations it can be seen that:-

    a) capacity of exit staircases = 3872 (1936 x 2)

    b) capacity of concourse = 6153 (3491 + 2662)

    c) capacity of gateway = 4259

Terrace capacity is 3872 unless other limiting factors apply. If staircase capacity at (a) is increased to more than 4259 the restricting element in the exit system will be gateway (c) provided that the restricting elements on the concourse (b) can also accommodate the increase.

329. The capacity of the emergency exit system is calculated in the same way but using the relevant emergency evacuation time and the exit routes to the playing area and thereafter to outside the ground available for use in an emergency.

Figure 14.1
Assessment of exit capacity

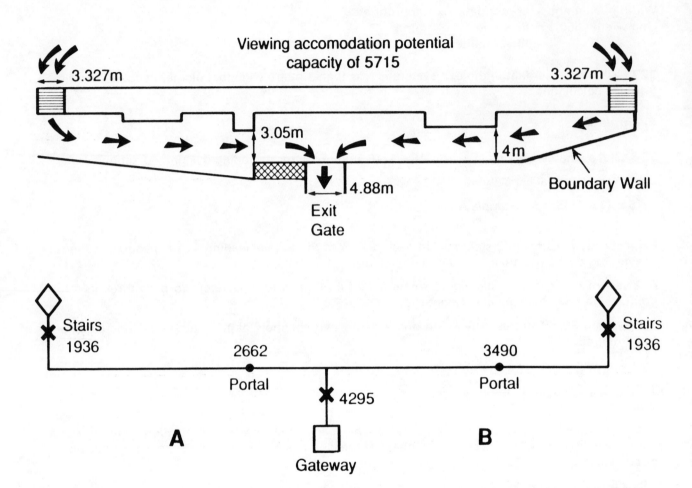

Example G

330. Details as in example F assuming that (a) emergency evacuation time is judged to be $2^1/2$ minutes; (b) normal exit route is available for use in an emergency; (c) additional emergency exit routes to the playing area are available by means of 4 gangways at 1.1 metres each (see Figure 14.2).

Staircase $\dfrac{3.327}{.550}$ x 40 x $2^1/2$ = 604.9 (605)

Portal $\dfrac{3.05}{.550}$ x 60 x $2^1/2$ = 831.8 (832)

Portal $\dfrac{4.00}{.550}$ x 60 x $2^1/2$ = 1090.9 (1091)

Gateway $\dfrac{4.88}{.550}$ x 60 x $2^1/2$ = 1330.9 (1331)

4 gangways at 1.1 = $\dfrac{4.4}{.550}$ metres x 60 x $2^1/2$ = 1200.

Capacity of the normal exit system is governed by the staircases: 605 x 2 = 1210

Capacity of the exit system to pitch = 1200

Total = 2410

Figure 14.2.
Emergency exit routes (see example G).

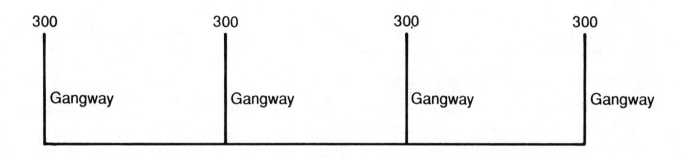

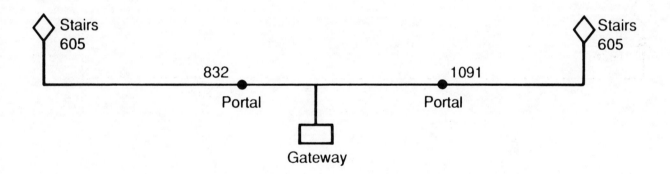

20. RECOMMENDED FLOW RATES

331. The flow rates quoted below are the maximum rates and are for purposes of calculation only. They assume that movement is through an exit-width of at least 1.1 metres (ie. a double unit-width) and that underfoot conditions comply with those recommended elsewhere in the Guide. If, in an individual case, it is evident from studies of crowd movement at a ground that a lesser flow rate is actually achieved from those mentioned, the actual rate should be used for calculation purposes.

332. From stands and all stairways a flow rate of 40 persons per minute per unit of exit width (ie 550 mm) should be used.

333. From terraces (including covered terraces) and the ground generally a flow rate of 60 persons per minute per unit of exit width should be used.

ANNEX A

MANAGEMENT RESPONSIBILITY: WRITTEN POLICY OF SAFETY

The safety policy for spectator safety is, in effect, an extension of that drawn up by management in respect of staff. It should make clear that there is a duty on all employees to ensure, as far as they are able, that all activities which take place at the ground are conducted in such a way that, as far as is practicable, the safety of everybody at the ground is assured. The policy should identify the safety objectives and the means of achieving them and should include at least the following "10 point plan".

1. *Organisation/Structure* for implementing safety.

2. *Arrangements* to monitor the policy (at all levels).

3. *Crowd Management:* to include

    a) entry - identification of and admission to each section of viewing accommodation.

    b) exit - movement across, on leaving the viewing accommodation and thereafter.

    c) accommodation - occupancy level, division, seating, crush barrier requirements.

4. *Stewarding:* to include determination of minimum numbers, location, training and supervision.

5. *Inspection and Safety Audits:* to include identification, tests, checks of structural elements.

6. *Communications*

    a) to the public.

    b) internal - police - emergency services.

7. *Fire Precautions.*

8. *First Aid/Medical Provision.*

9. *Emergency Action Plan* (in association with the police and emergency services).

10. *Maintenance of Records* - attendances, incidents, inspections, tests, measures taken.

ANNEX B

FIRST AID, MEDICAL FACILITIES AND AMBULANCES

General

1. The measures described elsewhere in the Guide will, if followed, help to prevent a serious accident but for ground management to discharge fully their safety responsibilities they should ensure that proper first aid and contingency medical provision is available in case there is an incident. This means that, normally, there will be an NHS ambulance service presence at the ground where a crowd of over 5,000 is expected (see paragraph 7 below). In all cases, however, ground management should consult the local Health Authority's Chief Ambulance Officer of the ambulance service for the area to determine the ambulance, first aid and medical requirements for the ground. Where a safety certificate is in force the consultation arrangements should be made through or, if required, approved by, the relevant local authority.

First aid staff and accommodation

2. At each event there should be a minimum of 2 trained first aiders and at least one trained first aider per 1,000 spectators. The responsibility for securing the attendance of first aiders lies with ground management who should consult the Health Authority's Chief Ambulance Officer on the level of training required.

Accommodation

3. Ground management should provide accommodation designated for the provision of first aid to spectators. This should be in addition to the club's medical room. Any room set aside for this purpose should be large enough to contain a couch with enough space for people to walk around; a sink providing hot and cold water and drinking water; a worktop; and sufficient room to store stretchers, blankets and pillows. Toilet facilities should be available. The recommended minimum size of the room is 15 square metres. Where the authorised capacity of the ground exceeds 15,000 the size of the accommodation should, ideally, be increased to at least 25 square metres and an additional couch should be provided. Care should be taken to ensure that the doorway is large enough to allow access for a stretcher or a wheelchair.

4. First aid rooms should have heating, lighting, ventilation and electric sockets. The room should be signposted throughout the ground and located in such a position that it is accessible to both spectators and emergency vehicles. A telephone line should be installed allowing internal and external communication.

5. The first aid room should contain suitable storage for first aid materials and equipment, the nature of which should be agreed with the local Health Authority's Chief Ambulance Officer. Ground management should appoint someone with sole responsibility for the equipment and materials in the first aid room and for the upkeep of the room. These facilities should be available at any time for inspection by the NHS ambulance service officers.

Medical Practitioner

6. At matches or events where the number of spectators is expected to exceed 2,000, a medical practitioner able to manage accident and emergency situations should be present. The medical practitioner should have specific training in cardio-pulmonary resuscitation and in the use of automatic/advisory or manual defibrillators. The medical practitioner should (a) be at the ground at least an hour before the start of the event; (b) remain until half an hour after the end of it; (c) be made aware of the location and staffing arrangements of the first aid room(s) and details of the ambulance cover. The whereabouts of the medical practitioner should be known to first aid and ambulance staff and to those in the control room who should be able to make immediate contact with him or her.

Ambulance provision

7. Ground management should make arrangements for the provision of at least one fully equipped ambulance either from the NHS or, if from elsewhere, approved by the local Health Authority's Chief Ambulance Officer, to be in attendance at all events with an anticipated crowd of 5,000 or more. Any additional ambulance cover should be determined after consultation with the local Health Authority's Chief Ambulance Officer. The following provides a general guide to the ambulance service provision which, in most cases, would be considered reasonable.

Expected attendance	Ambulance provision
(a) 5000 to 25000	1 Accident and Emergency ambulance (with 2 paramedics); 1 Ambulance Officer
(b) 25000 - 45000	As in (a) above plus deployment of a major incident/equipment vehicle and 2 additional paramedics; 1 control unit
(c) 45000+	as in (b) above plus 1 additional ambulance (with 2 paramedics).

Ground management should note that should a serious incident develop the NHS ambulance service has the capability and command structure to build rapidly on the above resource in order to ensure the protection, treatment, care and medical evacuation of any casualties.

ANNEX C

TESTS AND INSPECTIONS

1. As indicated in Chapter 2 and Chapter 5, regular and detailed inspections of the ground are a necessary and important function of ground management. The following provides a tabulation of tests and inspections referred to in the text of the Guide.

Before each event

2. Check the operation of exit doors and gates including mechanisms securing them to ensure that they can be opened immediately in an emergency.

3. Test all automatic fire detection and fire warning, emergency lighting, public address and other communication systems 24 hours before an event.

4. Inspect and test turnstiles and monitoring systems to make sure they are in proper working order.

5. Check that the ground does not contain any accessible items which could be used as missiles.

6. Check that there are no accumulations of combustible waste, remove any hazardous materials from the premises, if possible, or make sure they are safely stored well away from public areas.

7. Check that all entry/exit routes are clear of obstruction, free from trip hazards, that surfaces are not slippery and that all such routes can be safely and effectively used.

8. Check that directional signs are in place and illuminated (where appropriate).

9. Ensure that sufficient numbers of trained stewards and first aid staff are present.

10. Ensure that first aid equipment and materials are maintained at the required level.

After each event

11. Carry out a general visual inspection for signs of damage which might create a potential danger to the public and take remedial action.

12. Clear away litter and inspect the ground to ensure that there are no accumulations of combustible waste.

Pre-Season/Mid-Season

13. Check the stewarding arrangements to ensure that all stewards have sufficient and effective training.

14. Test, by carrying out exercises, that emergency procedures operate smoothly.

Annually

15. Arrange detailed inspection of the ground, including boundary walls, fences, gates and all components and installations.

16. Arrange the visual inspection of all crush barriers and handrails and other structural elements.

17. Arrange the physical testing of a 25% representative sample of crush barriers and handrails and other structural crowd control elements. All elements should therefore be tested at least once every 4 years.

18. Visual inspection of all boundary walls, fences and gates.

ANNEX D

TESTING AND INSPECTION OF CRUSH BARRIERS, HANDRAILS AND OTHER STRUCTURAL CROWD CONTROL ELEMENTS

Objective

1. The objective of visual inspections and physical testing is to ascertain the condition and strength of the crush barriers and handrails and other elements in order to establish that they comply with the requirements of the Guide and that they are adequate to carry out their required function - ie that they will safely withstand the pressures generated by the movement of spectators during entry, viewing and egress. A factor of approximately 20% over and above the design load is used for the test load (see Table 2 Chapter 10).

2. Note: forces generated may vary depending upon the event, the size and nature of the crowd and its dispersal. Crowds at football matches including rugby who are essentially static throughout the match, occupying accommodation at a packing density of up to 47/10 square metres and who leave all together at the end of the game will probably generate greater pressure on barriers, handrails etc than spectators at other events such as cricket or athletics. The criteria for strength of handrails and barriers etc envisage the more robust nature of spectator movement and actions at, say, football matches.

Personnel and Equipment

3. The inspections and testing should be carried out by or under the supervision of a competent, suitably qualified engineer belonging to a recognised professional institution. The engineer will be responsible for ensuring that the inspections and testing are properly carried out and that all results are accurately recorded. The engineer must be satisfied that equipment used for the tests is suitable for the purpose and is used in the correct manner. The equipment used should be capable of a level of accuracy ± 5% of the test force. The deflection measuring equipment should be calibrated and be capable of a level of accuracy of ± 0.5 mm.

Records

4. Detailed records should be made and kept of all observations, loadings, deflection/recovery readings etc in respect of each structure inspected and tested. The record should include a standard record sheet identifying each barrier tested and inspected, its location (including cross-reference to the plan), date of inspection and comments and state clearly whether the barrier, handrail etc has passed or failed.

Inspections

5. All crush barriers and handrails etc should be inspected annually taking due account of comments recorded from previous inspections (see paragraph 4 above).

6. Any visible defects, such as corrosion, cracks, holes, misalignment, undue distortion, missing bolts or fittings, should be noted and their potential effect on the integrity and strength of the structure assessed in order to determine whether its condition is fit for its intended purpose.

7. If it is considered that members or connections, due to the nature of their construction, have hidden defects such as corrosion, further investigation should be made. This may involve partial dismantling if this can be done without detriment to the structure itself.

8. Particular attention should be paid to areas where corrosion or damage could result in a loss of performance ie water traps.

9. Should inspections result in any doubt as to the integrity or potential strength of the barrier or handrail etc it should be tested in accordance with the Guide or deemed to have failed.

Testing

10. Testing should be undertaken annually on a 25% representative sample of crush barriers and handrails etc throughout all parts of the ground. Each year the sample should be different so that all crush barriers and handrails are tested at least once every 4 years. The 25% sample does not include any which, following inspection, are tested as a result of doubts as to their integrity.

11. The method of physical testing should be as given below.

Test Method

12. The test is in two parts: Bedding In Cycle and Proof Cycle. In each part an evenly distributed force is applied horizontally on the top rail of the barrier or handrail at right angles to the longitudinal axis and is applied in increments. Crush barriers and handrails must comply with the requirements of both parts of the test in order to be considered satisfactory for further continued use.

13. The deflection measuring equipment should be properly set up on a firm part of the terrace, stairway etc, unaffected by any movement of the barriers or handrail. The deflection in the horizontal plane should be measured at the anticipated location of maximum deflection, eg at the centre of a barrier or handrail span (when testing the rail) or the top of the upright (if testing the upright).

Bedding In Cycle

14. In order to allow for the bedding in of the test equipment and any frictional restraints, the barrier or handrail should be loaded up to its design service load (see Table 2 Chapter 10). The bedding-in force should be applied in at least 5 equal increments. Deflections should be monitored at each increment of the load cycle. The maximum force should be maintained for 5 minutes.

15. The barrier or handrail may be considered to have completed this part of the test satisfactorily if, on removal of the force, the recovery is at least 75% of the maximum deflection as measured from the original position prior to loading or if the permanent deflection is less than 2 mm. If the barrier or handrail fails to achieve this level of recovery it shall be considered to have failed the test unless there is a satisfactory explanation for the results.

Proof Cycle

16. The proof cycle is to consist of two consecutive applications of the proof force, the interval between each application should be as short as practicable, ie to enable complete unloading.

17 For crush barriers the proof force is either 6.0 kN/metre width or 4.1 kN/metre width of barrier as mentioned in Chapter 9.
For handrails the proof force is either 4.1 kN/metre width or 2.7 kN/metre width of handrail as mentioned in Chapter 9.

18. Each of the two applications of proof force should consist of 5 equal increments, the full proof force being maintained for 5 minutes for each application. A record should be kept of any deflection during loading, maintained loading, or unloading (see paragraph 4 above).

19. If, on removal of the force after the second application the recovery is at least 95% of the maximum deflection or the permanent deflection is less than 2 mm (as measured from the barrier position at the start of the proof test cycle - ie after the bedding in cycle), the barrier or handrail should be considered to have satisfied the proof cycle loading requirement.

Other Considerations

20. Wherever possible comparison should be made with the performance of other crush barriers of a similar type and with the same barrier previously subjected to the same or similar tests in order to establish whether there are indications of a reduction in overall performance which might indicate a developing weakness requiring special attention or more frequent testing and/or inspection than the minimum.

21. If at any time during the procedure, and notwithstanding that the barrier or handrail has satisfied the test requirements, doubt arises for any reason (including such matters as corrosion, cracking of the terracing stairway etc or distortion of connections) as to the safety of the barrier or handrail, a detailed investigation should be carried out. Unless the results of this investigation remove the doubt as to the safety of the barrier or handrail, the barrier or the handrail as the case may be, should be deemed to have failed.

22. The principles of the testing procedure recommended in previous editions of the Guide are still valid as are the results of such tests until re-testing is required under paragraph 10 above.

ANNEX E

STEWARDING (See Chapter 16)

1. Stewards should be fit, active, not less than age 18 and ideally not more than 55 years of age. All stewards should be capable of carrying out their duties and should be properly trained to do so.

2. Stewards must be informed in writing of all that they are expected to know and do. It should be made clear to them that they are deployed to assist in the safe operation of the ground not to view the event.

3. The following list gives examples of typical tasks and duties which stewards should be expected to carry out and for which they should be prepared. Each steward should be given a written summary of the tasks, duties and responsibilities for the particular post to which he or she is allocated. Stewards should:

    i. Monitor the crowd throughout the ground for signs of distress or overcrowding and take action in accordance with standing instructions.

    ii. Prevent overcrowding by ensuring the crowd limits in various parts of the ground are complied with.

    iii. Prevent spectators, as far as possible, from climbing fences and other structures eg floodlight pylons, and from standing on seats. (Where by virtue of the scale of the incident stewards are unable to prevent this, they should immediately report the matter to the nearest police officer or, if no police officer is present, to the chief steward or the safety officer.)

    iv. Staff all parking areas to ensure all approaches and emergency exits are kept clear and that vehicles are correctly parked.

    v. Ensure that gangways and exits are kept clear.

    vi. Staff all exits including openings in perimeter fence.

    vii. Assist in the diversion of spectators to other parts of the ground including the closing of turnstiles when the capacity for any area is about to be reached.

    viii. Identify and investigate any incident or occurrence among spectators, reporting their findings to the police or to management.

    ix. Know the location of and be able to operate effectively the fire-fighting equipment at the ground.

    x. Know the location of the first aid room and any first aid equipment kept elsewhere.

    xi. Be fully conversant with any methods or signals used to alert staff that an emergency has arisen.

    xii. Be capable of recognising potential fire hazards and suspect packages, reporting such findings immediately to the nearest police officer or, if no police officer is in the immediate vicinity, the chief steward or the safety officer.

    xiii. Comply promptly with any instruction given in an emergency by a police officer, the chief steward or the safety officer.

    xiv. Remain at their allocated posts as instructed unless authorised or ordered to do otherwise by a police officer, the chief steward or the safety officer.

    xv. Report to the safety officer any damage or defect which is likely to pose a threat to spectator safety eg a damaged crush barrier.

    xvi. Assist in the prevention of pitch invasion.

    xvii. Assist as required in the evacuation of the ground.

    xviii. Assist in the identification of spectators who are banned from the ground or who do not possess tickets at all ticket matches or who are in possession of forged tickets.

    xix. Assist in the prevention of breaches of ground regulations.

71

ANNEX F

GLOSSARY

Lateral Gangway – channel for the passage of spectators through viewing accommodation running across the slope parallel with any terracing or seat rows.

Radial Gangway – channel for the passage of spectators through viewing accommodation running with the slope between any terrace steps or seat rows. The gangway will be stepped between tiered seating.

Stairway – that part of a building or structure which is not a radial gangway but which comprises of at least one flight of steps, including the landings at the head and foot of steps and any landing in between flights.

Viewing accommodation – gross area of that part of the ground or building in the ground provided for spectators to view the event.

Place of safety – a place where a person is no longer in danger from fire or other emergency.

Fire door – a door which will resist fire for a stated period of time (when subjected to a test under BS 476). Such doors are self-closing.

Fire resistant – ability of a component or construction to resist fire for a stated period of time (when subjected to an appropriate test in accordance with BS 476).

Flammable – able to burn with a flame.

Combustible – able to burn.

Local authority – as in the Safety of Sports Grounds Act 1975 ie

(a) in London, the borough council;

(b) in metropolitan districts - the metropolitan district council;

(c) elsewhere in England and Wales - the county council;

(d) in Scotland - the regional or islands council.

INDEX

Printed in the UK for HMSO Dd 0293650 C20 4/91 488 12521